The Daily T

Diary of a
Farming Wife

One woman's view of the
foot and mouth crisis

Sally Leaney

MERTON PRIORY PRESS

First published 2001

Published by
Merton Priory Press
67 Merthyr Road, Whitchurch
Cardiff CF14 1DD

ISBN 1 898937 51 6

Printed by
Dinefwr Press Ltd
Rawlings Road, Llandybie
Carmarthenshire SA18 3YD

Contents

List of Illustrations

Picture Credits

Plates 1–3 and 6–13 Abbie Trayler-Smith; Plates 4, 5 and 14 and back cover Sally Leaney; front cover Andrew Snell.

Preface

Writing this book has taken me along a new and exciting journey but has been a team effort. As Duncan says, there is no 'i' in the word 'team', so I am glad to have this opportunity to thank my friends:

Sue Ryan at *The Daily Telegraph*, who gave me the initial opportunity to write and helped to open new doors in my life.

Philip Riden at Merton Priory Press, for his help and support in publishing my first book.

Abbie Trayler-Smith for her wonderful photographs. She overcame eight hours of continuous rain but was rewarded with two cows calving on cue, in the right place at the right time.

Andrew Snell, a friend and very patient and able photographer, who agreed to the challenge of working with both children and animals to take the front cover picture.

Jilly, my dear friend, who has so bravely climbed her own personal mountains, and was able to read my writing, correct my spelling and type this book.

My loving parents, who have always supported me, even when I wanted to be a lady-farmer. Without the use of their dining room table (my temporary office away from the farmhouse telephone) and the drinks at twelve, lunch at one, and tea at four this book would never have been finished.

Alice and Sam, who would be furious if they didn't get a mention.

Duncan, whose positive attitude and outlook on life is a constant reminder to me to smile and be grateful for what we have. No one could work harder for his family than Duncan.

And finally, I would like to dedicate this book to the memory of Michael Stanbury, our 74-year-old student, who was always there for us. His spirit is very much part of Heale Farm.

I sincerely hope that this book helps to continue to focus attention on the foot and mouth crisis until plans and policies are put in place to ensure that never again will death and destruction devastate what is dear to so many of us.

Heale Farm   SALLY LEANEY
September 2001

Introduction:
Learning to be a Farmer

How it all began

The midday news announces that foot and mouth has been discovered in pigs in an abattoir in Essex. My initial reaction? Essex
is a long way away, isn't it, and they'll keep it under control,
won't they? Drive on, I'm late for the dentist.

Sometimes you hear or read something and have no idea what
effect that something is going to have on your life. Five minutes
earlier foot and mouth was something most of us knew little about.
For 35 years the phrase, like the virus, had laid dormant in this
country.

How could I have ever imagined how many peoples' lives
would be affected? How could I have known that millions, yes
millions, of innocent and probably healthy farm animals would be
slaughtered? How could I have ever known that the fragile crust of
survival on most farms would be destroyed, possibly for ever?

No other news story in peace-time would ever prove to domi-
nate the radio, the television and the newspapers for the next few
weeks and months as much as the foot and mouth crisis has. Day
after day, week after week, burning pyres dominated the headlines.
Images of black charred legs rising from the flames scarred our
minds. Dead animals were shovelled into lorries and tipped like
bags of rubbish into pits or on to pyres. New words crept into our
language and became part of our everyday life. Words such as
'biosecurity', 'contiguous cull', 'slaughter on suspicion', 'FMD'
and 'C and D'.

We watched grown men, farmers with strong, rugged features,

sob on primetime television. The cynical suggested the animals were to die anyway, so what's the difference, and accused some of crocodile tears. Anyone with an ounce of understanding of the relationship between the farmer and his animals would appreciate the gut-wrenching terror the farmer feels when an army of white-suited Ministry vets arrive at the farm gate.

Our hearts ached for the children who have seen things they should never have seen at their age. Pet lambs and calves have been destroyed but slaughtermen had little time for a good bedside manner, they just had a job to do. Two little boys tried their hardest to save their pet lambs and hid them in their wardrobe. Imagine the dilemma of the parent who had to take on the role of Judas for the good of the nation. Or the little girl in Devon whose job was to spray the rotting carcasses every day in her father's yard to keep away the flies and the smell.

Who could predict that schools would close, villages would go into mourning and markets would shut? Animal movements were halted, but a week too late. A week in which thousands of animals' movements, primarily sheep, would prove to have dire consequences.

The whole way of life so familiar to those living in the country would change. Even occasional visitors would be banned from setting foot on public land meant to be shared by us all.

A nervous ripple spread out amongst people terrified that they might be the one to spread the disease. Farms became isolated and farmers developed a siege-like mentality against the silent killer. Churches, doctors and social workers responded to the crisis and set up an 'at risk' list. But for some it was too late and the crisis claimed a group of farmers too.

And then, like a pack of playing cards, the knock-on effect began. The public cancelled their holidays, hotels stayed empty and the M5 was clear of caravans. We saw footage of American TV news showing the whole of the UK as one giant burning pyre. Terrified, the Americans stayed away and so did their dollars.

As foot and mouth hit tourism and this year's holiday trade the pressure increased on Tony Blair. He dared to suggest that 'the crisis was under control' in a desperate attempt to save his precious election date. Downing Street became blinkered. They saw what they wanted to see, heard what they wanted to hear and ignored the rest. Everything they did had a political undertone. All that mattered was the election date of 7 May.

The countryside needed order, it needed help, it needed the Army. But to call in the Army was to admit that the country was in crisis. A country in crisis could not hold an election. The election was more important to Mr Blair and his Government than a few animals who were due for slaughter anyway.

Then the experts played with the figures and produced a model. They predicted 4,000 cases in June, with the peak still to come. Nick Brown, the Agriculture Minister, shuffled in his seat and his palms became even more sweaty. Even in his wellies he did not inspire confidence; concern yes, but not control.

Rotting carcasses lay stinking in farmyards to add to the terrible loss and shock being endured. Some farmers had carcasses in their yards for over two weeks. Farmhouse windows stayed shut and the bodies were a constant reminder of a living hell. Animal bodies finally fell to pieces when it was time to load them on to the trailers. Black binliners were tied around the cows' heads in a pathetic attempt to stop the spread of the virus by vermin, rats, foxes etc. My heart goes out to the person who had to do that job.

In a case of double standards the Government were grateful to the huntsmen who proved to be such efficient slaughtermen, but time will tell if their services are to be remembered.

Others had to hold one-day-old lambs as they were given a lethal injection. Some ewes lambed in shock as the flock were being slaughtered but the newly born, damp lambs still had to be killed. Farmers' wives still got up in the night to help a ewe lamb, even though they were to be slaughtered in the morning. A local headline in a Devon newspaper declared 'Silence of the Lambs' which summed up the whole situation. And finally the pressure was too much, the election was postponed and the Army called in. Never before in peace-time had any event caused an election to be postponed. Such was the scale of the crisis and the potential cost to the country.

Nick Brown was offered a back seat and we could all relax as

Mr Blair himself was now in charge. But after months of dithering it would not be that easy. A virus does not follow government rules but reinvents its own statistics.

The priority was simple. Reduce the time from diagnosis to slaughter to 24 hours and the virus could be controlled. That became the number one focus. In some areas previous mistakes and delays meant that the virus was jumping from farm to farm faster than the vets could diagnose it.

Suddenly the public had seen enough death and the tide turned. The need to cull such large numbers of animals was questioned. Were all contiguous culls necessary? Should blood test results be confirmed rather than continue the practice of slaughter on suspicion?

Individuals took a deep breath, sought legal advice and challenged the Government. 'Phoenix', the photogenic white calf, arose from the ashes as a symbol of survival against the odds. Farmers questioned whether the culling on such a large scale was doing any good. Up until then farmers were prepared to sacrifice their herds and flocks, after years of breeding, so as to spare their neighbours. But the speed and pattern of spread raised some questions. Lawyers found loopholes suggesting that the Government was even acting illegally in some contiguous culls. I suspect this issue still has a long way to go.

Tourism sank deeper and deeper. But 'the countryside is open', declared the Government, as ministers took it in turns to dust the cobwebs off their wellies and invite the cameras for a stroll. Tourists were confused, farmers were confused, but the slaughter continued and continued and continued. The question of vaccination was repeatedly raised but never completely answered. Although used successfully in France and Holland, our politicians could not make up their minds.

The Government embarked on a well-orchestrated programme of spin to deflect the blame. Farmers were accused of earning too much out of the crisis and even of spreading the disease themselves. I sincerely hope the public will be able to identify fact from fiction and recognise that the Government scored an own goal from one spin too many.

But meanwhile the foot and mouth crisis still has a long way to run. A Cumbrian farmer has achieved the unwelcome distinction of being the 2,000th infected farm and in all almost four million animals have been slaughtered. The virus continues to outwit man's ingenuity and so still the animals die.

Why did I start a diary? After my initial naïveté I was aware that the disease could jump from Essex to Yorkshire in only two short days. A virus has no respect for man and his boundaries. This outbreak had the potential to be big. I am by nature someone who likes facts and details and it seemed natural to me to record what effect this disease could have. In particular, how it would affect our family at Heale Farm.

At the time of the outbreak Duncan and I, who farm together at Heale Farm in Somerset, were just beginning to calve our 90-cow dairy herd. Our partnership works well as we have different strengths and abilities. Duncan is incredibly strong, an excellent bovine midwife and a positive thinker who can usually find a solution to most problems. Being a typical farmer he prefers the solution not to cost too much.

As for myself, Duncan simply says I am just 'naturally bossy'. I prefer to call myself 'full of management ideas'. But he does agree I make a good cup of tea when he's milking.

We have two children, Alice (12) and Sam (10). Alice is a 'doer' with a strong determined character. 'I wonder where she gets that from', Duncan reminds me regularly. But it takes two to tango, I reply. Sam is more artistic, doesn't really like dirty farmyards and takes life at a gentler pace.

Have I always wanted to farm? Initially I would have liked to have been a vet and so set up my own surgery at home when I was younger. As we only had one pet, Tabitha, a very loving tabby cat, my potential was limited. But Tabitha was 'booked in' at half-hourly intervals for a variety of ailments. One day she escaped downstairs after having suffered a very severe but imaginary road traffic accident. All four legs were tied in 12-inch ruler splints but she made her bid for freedom. I still don't know how she made it downstairs when so heavily bandaged but I suspect it was pure survival instinct.

But I did have a love of all animals, cows in particular, and the English countryside. Wanting to farm as a girl nearly thirty years ago whilst living in suburbia and not knowing anyone who farmed was quite a challenge. The careers teacher had to search deep down for details of agricultural courses and advice. But I remember being told by someone much older and wiser than myself that if you want to do something badly enough then you can overcome anything to do it.

So I set about being a farmer.

Sussex

Before agricultural college you were expected to work for a year on a farm. Having no agricultural links, we relied on the college for contacts. Would a farmer be prepared to take a complete novice? Would I be an asset or a liability? How would I know which was the right farm for me?

Following up one lead, we drove into the deepest depths of Mid Wales to a farm with Jersey cows. They usually employed a gang of three or four students, which sounded fun, but at 18 years old Wales seemed a long way from home.

I also went to an interview at a farm in Sussex. I remember wishing so hard for the farmhouse to be as in my dreams. For years I had dreamt about a perfect farmhouse kitchen, with an Aga, a scrubbed kitchen table, the dresser full of old china, a comfy chair in which to read the *Farmers Weekly* and a collie by the door. Other friends at school had dreamt of boys and Mary Quant make-up.

Slate House Farm in Sussex was everything I could have hoped for. No Aga, but a larder full of chocolate biscuits from the cash and carry and two dogs instead. Michael and Doreen Shaxson made me feel very welcome. Michael felt it was important to support young people in farming. Each year he was prepared to employ a student, even one as naive as me. To find a farmer who would employ a newcomer, and a girl as well, was quite rare.

They invited me for a weekend. I remember the anxiety of what to wear. Today I have a bedroom full of farm clothes, but growing up in Surrey I had no need for overalls and wellies. I was so anxious to please, but desperately unsure of what they thought of me. I was offered a year's work. The first six months I would receive only board and lodging, but be paid a full wage for the last six months.

What a wonderful place it was. Michael ran the farm with his brother Alistair and they divided their time between stock and arable. Michael was a passionate Ayrshire breeder with three magnificent herds. The three were milked through three different parlours—an 'abreast', when the cows stand alongside each other in a row of six; a 'tandem', when six cows were milked at a time, three each side, one behind each other; and finally a 'herring-bone', the most modern unit. The farm, of over 1,200 acres, cropped winter wheat and spring barley. Maurice looked after a hundred breeding sows and reared the piglets to bacon weight.

This was a textbook farm, with so many opportunities for a girl who knew nothing. All the basics that I now take for granted had to be learnt, such as how to bed up a calf pen, how to fill a hay net, how to call in a herd of cows for milking or even the best way to cut a straw bale.

And as for tractors? Well, I quickly learnt I had a stock rather than a mechanical bias. Disasters included knocking down a shed when I hit the main support post at speed. This shed had stood for two hundred years, but collapsed in a few seconds. 'Sorry' simply wasn't enough. All the villagers flocked to see the disaster and I was even mentioned in the parish magazine.

Or when I trapped the heavy roller in a gateway with seemingly no way out unless I took the gate and gateway with me. Which is what I did. Every other tractor driver over the past fifty years had always steered the roller through the gateway, but not me.

One of my first jobs was to feed the bulling heifers, the teenage equivalent in the bovine world. Twenty teenagers, full of life, quickly assessed that I was a new girl from the way I was attempting to lift their bag of food. The bag weighed 25 kilos, a very great deal if you are not used to it. Somehow I dragged the bag off the back of the pick-up truck and climbed through the fence. I couldn't work out how to open the gate as both hands were clutching the bag. Then shock, horror, these twenty teenagers came to meet me, not walking politely but galloping at top speed. Clouds of dust lifted from their galloping hooves. This was the highlight of their day and they had no time for introductions. They were hungry. I panicked, dropped the bag, ran back through the fence and hid in the neighbouring churchyard.

The heifers mooed in disgust, as their troughs were empty. The three biggest bullies were eating all the cake from the discarded bag. I prayed that nobody had seen or heard me, but knew I had to collect the evidence and pick up the bag. If only I'd known that if I simply stood my ground and shouted 'Get back girls' they would have meekly waited for me to fill their troughs.

Harvest was a simply magical time. I was part of the bale hauling team, still a very manual affair with two of us stacking bales on top of the trailer while two men pitched up with pitch-forks. Loading a trailer is quite a skilled affair as we loaded nine bales high—over 300 bales a load. We roped each load, but it had to be secure as we travelled home down some very steep slopes and along the main road. What a reward to go home lying on top of the stack; completely illegal, I'm sure, but what a wonderful way to travel. We carted over 20,000 small bales that summer. I became slim (well almost), strong and tanned but bore the blisters on my hands for months.

One day a load did collapse. As the bales fell away from beneath us and we tumbled on to the road we were fearful of the cars following the tractor. Fortunately they missed us.

The following year the farm invested in mechanical bale handling equipment and eventually converted to using big bales.

Not all jobs were fun. 'Rouging', manually pulling wild oats from a growing crop of wheat, was my least favourite. The oats, if harvested, would spoil the sample of corn. Today these wild oats are sprayed out earlier in the season. But for us we had to walk up and down the rows of corn for what seemed days on end, whatever the weather.

I loved the pigs and Maurice is a brilliant pigman. The best job was checking and sorting the litters. Baby piglets are cute. To see

40 or 50 piglets rushing across the yard, squealing with delight, is a lovely sight. The toughest job was feeding the fattening pigs. I'm sure the noise level of 400 hungry pigs screaming in unison broke all legal levels, but they had to be fed twice a day. Once fed, the squealing stopped so it was in your best interest to get the job done quickly. The added bonus was the smell of the pig muck stored in tanks beneath the pigs. At the end of each feeding an eerie peace hung over the shed, other than a few grunts of contentment.

But farms are a dangerous place, as I learnt one day. Health and safety rules make sense but when you are young they are just a nuisance. Peter and I were riding home in the tractor, one on each wheel-arch (illegal), while Malcolm drove. To impress us he jumped out of the tractor while it was moving, ran alongside and then jumped back in. We laughed, so he jumped out again. This time, as he tried to jump back in, his foot slipped on the step and we saw him fall under the tractor. I can still remember feeling the tractor drive over him with a sickening thud. A second thud as the trailer went over him too.

Peter jumped into the driver's seat while I ran back to Malcolm, sick with what I might find. He was alive, but in a great deal of pain. There were no mobile phones in those days, so I stayed with him while Peter went for help. He was moaning with pain and going into shock. Thank God he survived, but had broken both legs and had internal bleeding. Michael was furious and we deserved everything he said. It has left me with enormous respect for machinery. It makes me angry when I see Duncan or a contractor take a risk simply believing it could never happen to them. Farms are not playgrounds.

I hope by the end of the year Michael and Doreen felt I had been value for money. Doreen's wonderful cooking tried to undo all the good the hours of bale hauling did. Michael gave me a launch pad for my career in farming and I shall always be grateful to him. Sadly he died a few years ago, but I hope he understood what my year in Sussex meant to me.

What a fantastic year. I fell in love with the Sussex countryside, the hills of the South Downs, the Ayrshire cows, the piglets, and Peter the cowman—but that's another story.

College

Having worked for a year it was hard to settle down at college—Seale-Hayne Agricultural College in Newton Abbot, which occupies a magnificent position on a hill overlooking Torbay with the hills and valleys of Dartmoor behind.

I soon made new friends and loved every day at Seale-Hayne. I met Lizzie Wallis on my first day and secured a very firm friendship, which is just as strong today. Perhaps it was something to do with the delicious flapjacks her mother used to make. Our treat was to picnic on Dartmoor with Cinzano and flapjacks when we finished exams.

As there were only five girls on a course of 95, we had plenty of choice. Rumour has it that Lizzie and I were a formidable team and hot property! We enjoyed being elected the rugby team mascot.

Not having been brought up on a farm was both an advantage and a disadvantage. The disadvantage was having to work hard learning every small detail, the sort of detail a farmer's son had known since he was a young boy. However, the advantage was having no pre-conceived ideas of how things should be done. I had no experience of 'Father does it this way, so it must be right'. I challenged a lot more of the issues and theories.

Life as a student was fun. Once during Rag Week we were 'auctioned' in the store ring in Newton Abbot market, having to first go over the weighbridge. The lucky farmer who bid the highest had four female agricultural students to do with what he wanted for the day—only agricultural duties of course.

Each week we went out for farm visits and after one such trip to a chicken farm we were aware of a gentle clucking from the back of the coach. Dave had made a personal protest against battery cages and offered a few chickens the chance for freedom. Was the invitation to a chicken curry meal the next day a coincidence or not?

One day I came back from a weekend at home to find the complete contents of my bedroom arranged in the mechanisation room. The bed was beautifully made, set up by the blackboard. Amazingly, the lecturer carried on as though nothing had happened.

Cornwall

Part of the course was a sandwich period on another farm. Once again I was blessed to find a second wonderful farm, this time at Newquay in Cornwall. Yet again the farmers, the Davey family, would influence my life and help my farming career.

The 500-acre farm produced milk, sheep, beef, corn and potatoes. A wealth of opportunity. The cows were milked through a rotary parlour, which formed part of a large and successful tourist venture called Dairyland Farm Park. This was the dream of the oldest member of the family, Rex Davey, today a dynamic octogenarian.

Milking in the rotary was a very relaxed affair as you stood still while cows slowly travelled on the merry-go-round. They quietly entered one at a time and walked off at the end of their 'ride'. Training new heifers to the system was fun but the parlour had a panic button to stop it going round. Of all the parlours I have milked, the rotary is my favourite. The pace is steady and gentle and consequently the cows are quiet and relaxed.

Milking was made even more interesting because of the visitors. Every afternoon up to a thousand tourists watched you milk, looking down from the viewing gallery. It was a very social affair as often they would call out to ask a question or clap when I finally milked a difficult cow. We were asked some amazing questions, such as 'Why don't the bottles break when you milk a cow?'. The lady imagined four bottles were placed under four teats and milked directly into them. She had no idea about milking parlours, pasteurisation or bottling plants.

Enid, Rex's younger sister, was and still is a very good friend. She gave me my love of flowers and gardening and took me for long walks across the beaches and cliffs after work. Using her mother's special recipe, she is the best pasty maker I know.

I met Primrose when I was in Cornwall. Primrose was a large white goat with a Roman nose and long spotty ears. She had been abandoned and left tied up in a field, so guess who picked her up. She then became part of my life and travelled everywhere with me, sitting up like a dog in the back of my Citroen Diane. Every time we stopped for petrol she caused much amusement.

One weekend I had to go home, so Primrose came too. Clean, tidy suburban Surrey is not well equipped for a farm animal. But my Mother, having watched *The Good Life* on television, did her best and turned the side driveway into a makeshift pen. I don't think Primrose and I realised how much this disturbed my parents' routine, but they were marvellous. That is, until Primrose pruned the roses a little too hard. One afternoon we took her for a walk out through the churchyard and met the churchwarden. As we chatted Primrose, becoming restless, could wait no longer and produced a giant wee. As the church is on a slope, a steady stream flowed down the path through the lychgate and past the early evening worshippers. Apparently, they still talk about it today.

We all returned to college for the final year and exams. Primrose came too and produced two adorable white kids during our last term. She even appeared on our float during Rag Week.

Milk Marketing Board

At the end of college I faced a choice: stay on for a management course or find a job. I attended an interview in London for a job as a farm consultant with the Milk Marketing Board. I went through the whole day's interview with the zip of my dress undone (discovered in the ladies' loo at Waterloo station on the way home) but was still offered the job.

The initial training was an excellent combination of monthly courses and working in the field alongside established consultants. I became very aware of how much I had to learn and made plenty of mistakes. Such as in Norfolk when I declared my surprise to a farmer, 'Why do you grow stubble turnips when you have no cows?' and I received the curt reply, 'This is sugar beet not turnips'. Being able to identify the crop would be a major advantage in my job.

Farm consultancy was a fascinating job and I felt quite privileged to be welcomed into people's lives and to take part in their business decisions. As farming is a way of life it is virtually impossible to split personal and business affairs. I was frustrated at not being able to do more for people, being limited by time and workload.

Some farmers become very reliant on you. For example, one year a farmer rang me to advise him on what height Christmas tree he should buy.

The Milk Marketing Board employed over 90 consultants of whom only two were women. I think the female characteristic of being fundamentally interested in people was an advantage in the job. I remember being told, 'We have two ears and one mouth—use them in that proportion'. What a sound piece of advice. Being a good communicator is the key to being a good consultant.

But yes, being a woman did put me in some difficult situations on farms sometimes. Inevitably, some farmers did overstep the mark which could make follow-up visits embarrassing. Do farmers' wives ever make passes at male farm consultants? I doubt it.

Duncan

I met Duncan in 1981 through Peter, a mutual friend. They had also been to Seale-Hayne but being younger than me meant we did not meet at college. As I was even more bossy at college, and Duncan only lived for beer, rugby and women, this was probably a good thing.

Duncan's first chat-up line at the end of a party at his cottage was 'Would you like to come and see my turkey pullets?'. Was this the equivalent of a 'rural etching'? Whatever, it worked.

When you meet your future husband for the first time do you know he is the one you will marry? I didn't, as I fell in love with his cows, especially No 18, and Duncan saw me as a cheap milkmaid. He told his grandfather he'd never marry a dolly bird but someone who must be able to milk. Is there a hidden compliment in there somewhere?

Our courtship was strange. We rarely went out except for 'gammon and egg (sunnyside up)' at the Berni Inn—as long as we finished milking by last orders. I milked the cows while Duncan played rugby and went out with the boys. But don't feel sorry for me. I loved every minute. Duncan said he knew it was getting serious when I planted four apple trees in the cottage garden.

We married in April 1984. The day was a great success, much to my parents' relief after the rather eventful shopping trip to London. After arranging the wedding list at Peter Jones we walked to Laura Ashley to buy the bridesmaids' dresses. My father and Duncan chose to sit with the other bored looking men by the windows, while the ladies browsed. A disturbance started outside on the street. Duncan, the 'country boy', did not appreciate that the normal reaction in London is not to get involved and ran outside. A group of big, burly men were fighting and shouting. Duncan, ever mindful of the 'underdog' thumped the bigger man who was restraining a smaller man, kneeling on the pavement. My hero? Not quite. The man whom Duncan had hit stood up and shouted 'We're the police—I'll get you later'.

Duncan fled back into Laura Ashley and the assistants ushered him into the changing rooms to hide him. They warmed to his 'it wasn't my fault' look.

The big police officer, having bundled the criminal into a police car, came into the shop to look for Duncan. 'Where is he?', he demanded. My mother, fearing the wedding may have to be moved to Wormwood Scrubs, was about to throw herself to the mercy of the police and beg forgiveness when his radio called him away. Duncan sheepishly reappeared from the changing rooms, much to my parents' relief.

Walking back down Sloane Street, Duncan and my father had swapped jackets in case the police had put out a description. Duncan, wearing a smart double-breasted ex-Naval jacket three sizes too small, was not too convincing. My poor mother only returned to some form of normality after her fourth glass of red wine in Peter Jones's restaurant.

After this the wedding was a relatively quiet affair, but it made for an amusing best man's speech.

Farming at Heale

Duncan and I farm Heale Farm. When I first met him he was farming Corfe and Heale Farms with his father. His father took on the tenancy after having managed the herd at NIRD Reading. Duncan grew up wanting only to farm. He chose his bedroom because it looked out across the yard towards the cows and he spent all his time out on the farm. Perhaps that is why he is no good at washing-up!

Duncan has two sisters—Jenny, who lives in France, and Bridget, now a single mother who continues to bring up her children in Greece.

Corfe, a very pretty village, nestles under the Blackdown Hills. Only one main road passes through the village, the B3170, which continues up Corfe Hill and towards Honiton and the A303.

Historically, the area produced lime which was burnt in local kilns and brought down from the hills. Field names such as Kiln Close recall the history. Another field, Quoits Field, is adjacent to the hanging tree used by Judge Jeffries who presided at the assize court at Taunton: 'Quoits' refers to the hangman's rope.

Ten years ago Duncan's father wanted to retire. We bought him out and Duncan became sole tenant. Since then the value of our farming assets have crashed. Then we paid 70p per litre for quota. Today it is valued at 13p per litre, but it has given us the opportunity to farm on our own.

Twenty years ago the farm of 400 acres and two dairy herds supported two families and employed six staff. Today a farm of 300 acres and one herd is run by Duncan and two part-time staff. Twenty years ago heifers (first-time calvers) were worth 1,000 guineas (£1,050)—today you can buy a good milker for £500. Wheat sold for £120 per tonne, whereas last year we received £58 per tonne. Inevitably, our overheads have continued to rise over the same twenty years.

I often worry that the public image of farmers is of a 'moaning landowner driving his S-reg Range Rover'. But we are a mixed bunch. As tenant farmers, driving an E-reg Carlton, we are in a very different situation.

Throughout our twenty years at Heale the price of farmland has continued to rise. But why? In purely business terms no farming enterprise will produce a return on capital to finance land at over £2,000 per acre. But land, it seems, is still a good buy for any investors or farmers looking to expand, borrowing on the back of their existing farm business.

Recent farm losses can be offset against land values for owner-occupiers, but for tenant farmers such as ourselves it is a very different story. Most tenants I know have had to realise any private savings to keep the bank happy. Overdrafts are reaching new levels.

We rent 300 acres on the permanent tenancy and 100 acres of annual grass keep. This is good wheat ground provided the conditions are right for drilling in early October. We crop a rotation of two years winter wheat and one year winter beans with compulsory set-aside.

For the past ten years we have used contractors to plant, spray and harvest the crops. Financing modern machinery is out of the question for a farm of our size. When the silage team arrive there is over £250,000 worth of machinery in the field at any one time. I look at the forage harvester and think that's equivalent to a 'house on wheels'.

We have some good help on the farm. Mike, our 74-year-old student, who sadly died during the period covered by the diary, worked with Duncan, and previously his father, for over 25 years. Mike, a man of Exmoor, was a true countryman. He had a great understanding of rural life and was an excellent stockman. This is why our cows are so quiet. He tried to retire three times, but we kept finding him extra jobs to do. He threatened that this year it was for real. We shall miss him. Barry does some relief milking, enabling Duncan to have a day off on Sunday.

Bill, who lives in a cottage on the farm, is a sprightly octogenarian. He has the most wonderful memories of farming in Somerset 60 years ago when horses ploughed and hay was made in ricks.

Cows: a beginner's guide

We milk between 95 and 100 black and white cows. To improve milk yields we upgraded the traditional British Friesian cow by using Holstein semen from Canada and America. Although these tall, leggy cows are efficient milk machines they cost a lot to maintain and do not last for as many years. We have now gone back to using more traditional Friesian cows. As ever, farming has turned full circle.

The cows are spring calving, which means they calve between February and May. The date cows calve is purely a management decision to suit each individual farm. Our reasons for spring calving are to cut down on the winter workload, a dry cow being much simpler to look after than a milking cow, and to reduce the cost of production per litre.

Christmas 2000 was wonderful. This was the first Christmas since the children were born that we did not milk and could watch them open their presents. Duncan could actually indulge at lunch and sleep it off rather than having to go out and milk for four hours. What a difference it made.

The cows are loose-housed which means they have access to a big straw yard for sleeping. Previously we had cubicles (8 ft by 4 ft man-made divisions), enabling more cows to be housed in the same shed. Horrible things. Cows love being housed with plenty of straw. There is nothing more satisfying than seeing cows lying in deep straw quietly cudding (chewing food over and over to aid digestion). I love checking the cows in the evening when a peace descends over the barn and the cows doze in the straw.

I have a pet pig called Spot (Gloucester Old Spot). A grossly overweight, uneconomical sow is how Duncan describes her. She sleeps with the cows in the barn. Somehow she manages to 'steal' more than her fair share of straw, becoming totally hidden other than a pink nose sticking out. Usually she lies back-to-back with a cow, both leaning against each other, both fast asleep.

The best day in the year is when we turn the cows out for the first time in the spring. I love to get them excited by shouting 'Come on girls!' at top volume. Duncan has become old and boring and says we must keep them calm. They positively smile and run out of the yard, udders swinging from side to side. Even the oldest cows manage a skip and a jump.

We love our cows. Each one we have seen born, fed them from a bucket for the first time, seen them through the awkward teenage years and been there when they calve for the first time. Cows are incredibly loyal and well behaved provided you stick to a routine. The herd is full of individual characters.

No 45 is the lead cow. She brings the herd in for milking, leading the way every time. Where she goes the herd follows. No 96 is a devious eater and will sneak back into the parlour for extra helpings. No 80 is an obsessive mother who will walk through hedges or electric fences just to get back to her calf. No 73, the oldest cow and now almost grey, has seen it all before. She has produced over twelve calves.

The numbers are like names for our cows. Every time I see a number, such as the No 96 bus, I immediately think of one of our cows. Even my lottery numbers are my favourite six cows, dead and alive.

No 10 and No 14 are twins, both anorexic and living on their nerves, whereas No 87 simply lets the world go by without a single care. No 94 adores human contact and always stops to have her head scratched. But No 17 never gives us a passing look. No 67 is a walking miracle. Having damaged her back and been unable to get up for six weeks, she recovered to produce a handsome bull calf. Too weak to be shut in a shed or slippery yard she spent the winter 'roaming' the farm.

No 34 has produced twins in three successive years, but No 28 refuses to get into calf. I'm sorry to say that it will be her loss.

No 42 survived two twisted guts and two operations. Dear old No 112 was blind from birth, but you would never have known it. When, finally, she had to be put down, Duncan quietly held her in the barn rather than load her on a lorry for market.

Some cows are born with five or six teats instead of four. The extra ones have to be cut off. Ouch. Some are virtually all black or almost pure white. These white cows can be sensitive to the sun and No 2 has suncream regularly applied. No 70 only has one black spot on her shoulder so finding a place to freeze brand was very difficult. Every cow receives a freeze brand (her number) using a simple, painless procedure.

Some cows prefer the left hand side of the parlour and others the right. It is virtually impossible to drive them in on the side they do not want to go. There is no logical explanation to their preference as both sides of the parlour are identical to me. But then, I'm not a cow.

Bovine body shape and size is as varied as the human race. Fed virtually the same feed some cows put on weight and others stay quite thin. A fat cow is technically a poor feed converter, the feed having gone on 'her back' rather than in 'the bank'. No 77 should join me at Slimming World, whereas No 21 is equivalent to a dress size 8. Teat shape and size is also unique. Sometimes it is easier to identify a cow by her udder than her face as we spend more of our time studying the udder than looking them in the eye. No 60 has enormous fleshy teats, but No 20 has four tiny, petite teats almost too small to milk.

Feet and legs are crucial to a cow. We choose a bull for confirmation, especially for good feet and the right shaped legs. Duncan is an excellent chiropodist and much cheaper than the vet.

Each year we receive glossy pin-up magazines of the bulls available from all over the world. Their progeny are scored on confirmation, teat placement and milk yield. From these facts we choose the bull and order the semen. I wonder if I should hang up the bull pictures around the shed, so at least the cows know what their husband looks like.

Cows can make you laugh and make you cry (when they tread on your toe). You can love them or hate them (when they broke out on the night we used our electric blanket for the first time). They can be intelligent too. Last autumn after evening milking, No 107 walked back into the parlour. This was unusual as they all had fresh grass to eat. I could see something was wrong as the cow was blowing up in front of me. She stood still allowing me to reach into her mouth where I found a piece of apple lodged in her throat, which I quickly removed. The apple stopped the naturally produced stomach gases from being released which would undoubtedly have killed her. How did she know to come back to the farm for help?

So, when the threat of losing your herd because of the dreadful foot and mouth virus becomes very real, it is a terrifying thought. Cows of course have a limited life but to be slaughtered unnecessarily would be devastating. Cows offer us everything and as their custodians it is our duty to protect them.

1 Sally with Charolais calves, which eventually numbered over 80, kept on the farm because there was no market to which they could be sent.

2 Sally and Duncan help cow No 113 give birth. Good news! A healthy bull calf, but where do we put it? We are full up with calves everywhere.

3 The daily routine of lifting cow No 26 in the net, encouraging her to stand on her own. It took four weeks to achieve this. Now she is fit and well.

4 Our vet and his mobile office, showing some of the endless paperwork involved in issuing movement licences.

5 Our foot-dip, with Duncan spraying the straw mat at the entrance to the farm, the tension evident in his face.

6 Duncan feeding the cows.

7 The daily routine of cleaning the parlour after each milking. Moss joins in the fun.

8 Sally cleaning the milking parlour as the routine of twice-daily milking continues.

9 Duncan and Sally moving a freshly calved heifer into the herd to milk her for the first time.

10 The first feed for a newly born calf. The yellow ear-tag identifies each calf, who also each have individual passports.

11 Sally and Duncan's 12-year-old daughter Alice with one of the calves. Both children are encouraged to help on the farm during these busy times.

12 Some of the 80 calves kept on the farm because there was no market. Makeshift pens were made everywhere, with calves squeezed into every available corner.

13 Freshly calved cows on spring grass in March. Still no movement licence at this stage. Where do we graze next?

14 A ubiquitous symbol of the foot and mouth epidemic, closing one of the many footpaths which cross our farm.

The Diary
February

Wednesday 21 February. On the way back from Bristol ice-rink—a half-term treat for Alice and Sam—Radio 4 announces a foot and mouth outbreak in Essex. Duncan and I are shocked and surprised. We hope it is an isolated case and at least Essex seems a long way from Somerset.

We have just started calving. With 80 cows due to calve over the next ten weeks we are in for a busy time.

Alice decided today to adopt a calf of her own, so we welcome 'Treacle' into our family. Duncan set up the deal. £1 purchase price for Treacle (she is an Aberdeen Angus heifer calf and virtually worthless) and £1.50 for the cost of the official ear tags. The balance must be wrong when two tags are worth more than a life.

Let's hope it's a better year for milk. Last year we received an average of 14p per litre for our milk but our production costs were 18p per litre. As even the bank manager said, it costs us £20 for every milking. Crazy!

Thursday 22 February. The foot and mouth virus is now confirmed in three sites and more are under suspicion. Suddenly the country seems very small when I consider how easily it spreads. There is now a creeping anxiety in our lives and I freeze every time the news comes on the radio.

The postman tells me he can remember the dreadful smell of burning animals when he was a boy in the Midlands during the outbreak in the 1960s. That makes me shiver.

I take a friend in the afternoon to the oncology unit in Bristol which puts things in perspective.

Friday 23 February. 'FINAL STRAW—Farmers reeling again

under the Foot and Mouth disease ban' is the headline in the *Somerset County Gazette*. The Government has banned all meat and dairy exports.

What a cost to the industry, as we export £30 million of goods a week. Will those markets still be there when the ban is lifted? Our name is mud in Europe, but how did the virus come into this country in the first place?

I now listen to the news every hour—like waiting for a time bomb to go off. The Devon outbreak has been confirmed. That's getting alarmingly close.

The vet is still allowed on the farm and he arrives for the routine Ministry Brucella test (test for Brucellosis). A blood sample has to be taken from the base of the tail using a very sharp needle. The heifers had never been in the parlour before. The final scene was one of muck and chaos, nothing like the image of *Vets in Practice*.

We stop for tea and hot-cross buns, and Dick, our farm contractor, recounts the outbreak of foot and mouth in the 1960s when he was a boy on the family farm in Devon. His father developed a siege mentality, never leaving the farm and destroying the two farm collies to secure the farm's future.

This disease demands desperate measures. We ring the agricultural suppliers and order a 25-litre container of disinfectant. At £67 it's a cheap precaution. They reserved us the last one in the shop.

Well done to *The Archers* for writing the outbreak into their script so promptly.

Saturday 24 February. Six confirmed outbreaks and a seven-day ban on the movement of farm animals. We read in *The Daily Telegraph* that Ministry vets admit that the disease could have gone unreported for up to four weeks on the farm in Northumberland. Why, when lives and livelihoods are at risk of being destroyed?

After dropping Alice off at school I collect the disinfectant from the market suppliers. Taunton Market is empty. No noise, no bustle, no straw—what an eerie feeling. Television is doing interviews and the police are watching for anyone not following legal procedures. There is a very uncomfortable atmosphere. I dashed into the produce market and treated myself to three primrose plants and '2 for £1, out of date chocolate swiss rolls'. I needed chocolate and normality.

I set up a straw mat across the farmyard entrance and apply a good dose of disinfectant. It is a good feeling when I'm finished—I feel a little more in control.

Dick is finally drilling (planting) wheat. Unfortunately 50 acres of wheat we drilled early has failed, either having drowned or been eaten by slugs.

Duncan has gone to Twickenham for the day as a paid steward so Barry helps me milk this evening. It takes two of us to milk the new heifers—first-time calvers. Life has changed beyond all recognition for them. A few days ago they were 'not a care in the world' teenagers and now, having calved, they have responsibilities. 50 per cent are natural mothers but 50 per cent just want to get back to having a good time!

We have reared these heifers by hand since they were born and they all have individual characters. I know the quiet ones, the bullies and the 'cool girls'. They trust us and show tremendous loyalty.

I am so frustrated that they are my responsibility and there is nothing I can do to protect them from this virus.

Sunday 25 February. The Devon outbreak now looks very serious as the farmer is known to be a dealer and has eleven different farm sites.

Calving is not always a success. In principle it is a simpler process for the cow than a human. When the human race 'stood up' we produced a bend in our birth canal which causes all the problems. Poor No 26 (to us their numbers are names) has had a rotten time. She calved an enormous Charolais bull calf, sadly born dead, and has not been able to get up since, so I collected the cow lifting net from the vet yesterday.

Trying to pull, push and roll a 500 kg cow on to a net and raise her up with the tractor is tricky. After half an hour she is exhausted and we sit her back down again. We repeat the whole procedure at teatime and she rewards us by tucking into her tea, which is always a good sign.

It has taken Duncan and me over four hours to look after No 26. In economic terms this is a waste of money as she will not milk this lactation and may not even get back in calf.

But we are stockmen who love and respect our cows. Thank goodness that even in these desperate times we can let our hearts rule our heads and our bank balance—the day we lose this will be the time to sell up.

We have now taken every precaution possible to halt this dreadful disease. We have straw-soaked mats, foot-baths, sprayers to spray vehicle wheels and signposts politely asking people not to enter the farmyard. But are we doing enough?

We are amazed that we have received nothing from MAFF[1] regarding their advice on what we can do. Where does the virus live? Can it survive on the milk tanker, or on cardboard boxes if we take a delivery, or on human skin?

With so little knowledge I feel powerless.

Monday 26 February. 'Feel the fear—and do it anyway'. Since Friday Duncan and I have not spoken of our biggest concern. Are we insured against foot and mouth? We know that we will be compensated for any stock loss but what of consequential loss, such as loss of milk income?

Last year we seriously cut our levels of insurance to save costs. It seems we are both too scared to talk about it or look up the files.

When I face the fear and check the files, yes, we have kept up the insurance and will receive a payment for consequential loss—small but essential.

The news tonight reported NFU figures that show only 10 per cent of farmers are similarly insured. I am amazed. Perhaps it is a reflection of the recent drop in farming incomes.

The children are quite affected by the pictures of the burning animals, hundreds of cow legs rising above the flames. They are

---

[1] The Ministry of Agriculture, Fisheries and Food, superseded after the general election of June 2001 by the new Department for Environment, Food and Rural Affairs.

concerned that it might happen to our cows and ask whether the farm pets, particularly Misty, Alice's pony, and Moss, the farm collie, would have to be destroyed. Thankfully our neighbour Tim, a vet, reassures us all that this will not be necessary.

The March for Liberty and Livelihood has been postponed—I can appreciate why this decision has been made, but it seems that in the short term the Government has been let off lightly. We want the opportunity to march in our hundreds of thousands in London, we are not a silent minority.

Tuesday 27 February. Sixteen confirmed cases today. Somerset is still clear but we are sandwiched between outbreaks in Devon and Wiltshire.

With a ban on all animal movements we are experiencing two main problems. Firstly, this is our busy calving period and we would normally be selling calves to market, so the calf-pens are filling up fast.

Two Charolais twin bull calves have had four different mothers in the last 10 days. I am seriously wondering if they might suffer from an identity crisis. Mike suggested we build bunk beds. Good in theory.

Secondly, this will seriously affect our cash flow and our overdraft is already fully stretched. As tenant farmers we do not have the capital security of owner-occupiers.

I pick up Alice and Charlotte, her school friend, after cooking class. Charlotte's family are also farmers so I arrange to drop her at the end of their drive. We feel as though an invisible Berlin Wall has been built between us.

One of the positive outcomes of this outbreak has been the tremendous support we have received from friends. We have had so many phone calls simply to say 'we are thinking of you'. Others have come up to me in the playground and given me a hug. This means a lot to us. As someone observed, the countryside is forming a real sense of community in time of need.

Wednesday 28 February. Twenty-six cases recorded this morning and it seems the countryside is slowly shutting down. We farm alongside Taunton Racecourse and a meeting is planned for tomorrow. We are relieved to discover they have cancelled it.

Today is my mother's birthday and we meet for lunch at the village pub. The awareness of the threat is never far from our thoughts, but it helps to raise our glasses and we enjoy four superb fillet steaks—British beef at its best.

We are very short of feed for the cows and desperately need to order some more. Our dilemma is that the feed company is over the hills in Devon and the lorries have been visiting farms all over the South West. Our solution is to ask a neighbour, Brian, to collect the feed in his tractor and trailer. At least we know his trailer has not been out of his yard.

No 26 continues to fight for her life. Today she seems most indignant to be strung up in a net like a bag of Brussels sprouts.

The fresh calvers are out at grass for a couple of hours a day, which they love. One of the best signs in the farming year is to see cows go out to grass for the first time. If the movement ban continues we will not be able to utilise 80 per cent of our grazing as the cows have to go down the lane to reach it. All livestock are banned from walking on public roads.

March

Thursday 1 March. We woke today to hear the Chief Veterinary Officer suggest it will be an epidemic by next week. As they announce the new outbreaks we hold our breath as to whether it will be Somerset. So far we are clear—but for how long?

Played tennis with Andrea, Heather and Brenda, and as dog owners there was some confusion as to where they should and shouldn't walk. The parish council had received a directive from County Hall, and a decision has been made to close all footpaths across the parish. Problem solved.

A mutual friend, an auctioneer from North Devon, has been involved in the slaughter and valuation of stock in Devon. This has greatly distressed him. He is working a ten-hour day surrounded by tears and death.

Brian delivers the feed after lunch. Brian's visit is a relief to the cows as they have been on half rations for a few days and this morning we actually ran out of feed.

A new dilemma is that Misty the pony is desperate to be shod. Keeping on old shoes for too long could cause her to go lame, but we would not dare to have the blacksmith on the farm.

Friday 2 March. I feel panic this morning as four potential outbreaks have been announced in Somerset. One outbreak is only half an hour from here. This virus can travel at least 40 miles on the air—it makes a mockery of our disinfectant. I fear the noose is tightening.

Last night I was so distressed to read an article about a farmer's wife in Northumberland who had all her stock destroyed. I actually cried as I read her story—her husband showed such courage and stood with every one of his animals as they were being killed. I am determined to find that courage, if need be, for my cows too.

I am so angry that the BBC has a special programme tonight entitled *Do you trust British food?*. What a title! I can hear the nails being driven into the coffin.

With all our regulations, paperwork, accreditation and animal welfare programmes British food is the best and the safest. As I write, the Germans have exported to us beef with spinal cord. This is a disgrace and must leave the public feeling bewildered.

A lovely Charolais bull calf was born in the night. He is skipping around and looks wonderful, so there is good news as well as bad.

Saturday 3 March. The phone rings at 7 a.m. Brian asks if I saw the news last night. There is a suspected outbreak at Yarcombe in Devon. Yarcombe was where Brian collected the trailer of feed for us. I feel sick.

There are also three other suspected cases in Somerset. Duncan comes in and his whole mood changes. He says we are not doing enough to protect the farm and the cows. We argue, which is quite unlike us.

As I am driving Alice to school she calmly asks, 'Do you think Dad's the type to commit suicide?'. My heart misses a beat. 'What do you think?', I ask. 'No I don't think so', she replies and the subject is closed. Alice has obviously picked up the mood in the kitchen this morning. We must be more careful to protect the children and take time to listen to any of their worries.

We discover the suspected outbreak is in fact only five miles from us at the farm of a friend. We put down more dips and lay two disinfected straw mats on the road either side of the farm, and block the farm drive. Whether this does any good may be in doubt but at least we gain some strength from doing something. It will take up to four days to confirm the outbreak one way or another. We are now on a different level of fear and emotion.

Watched the BBC news tonight. Am haunted by the farmer who filmed his slaughtered stock as they lay in piles around his yard. He warned us never to watch your own stock being killed. The slaughter of the baby calves was the worst.

No 26 can now sit up like a dog but she needs strength in her hind legs to be able to stand. Late in tonight as two cows were calving. No 34 produced a giant. I really felt for her.

Sunday 4 March. It has snowed. The farm looks so tidy as all the rubbish and muck is covered in snow.

Duncan was up in the night as two more cows were due to calve. He is an excellent midwife, but has rather big hands. Fine if you are a cow, but if I was a sheep I wouldn't want him near me.

We seem to be on a roller coaster of emotion. It has just been announced that there is a confirmed outbreak on Dartmoor—this could have a devastating effect on the wildlife.

Each newly born calf is required to have a passport which goes with the animal right through its life. And all births, deaths and movements have to be recorded in the movement book. Yet more paperwork, but this outbreak proves that traceability is vital.

Monday 5 March. We are overwhelmed by the reaction of *The Daily Telegraph* readers to my diary which appeared in the paper today. We have received so many messages of support and advice from all over the country. I have laughed and cried on the phone with some wonderful people. It is a humbling experience for Duncan and myself.

Duncan is taking advice from an Army friend who has been trained in biological warfare, and the potting shed is now the decontamination room. Barry and Mike who work on the farm use it as a changing room to minimise the risk of foot and mouth.

The Pony Club rally was cancelled yesterday and Alice is unable to ride Misty across the fields to meet her friends.

We took four freshly calved cows away from their calves this morning in order to milk them full time. No 11 keeps calling for her calf, but the other three are desperate to be working mothers and get back into the herd. This is one aspect of dairy farming I do not enjoy.

The recent calves born are big and potentially may cause calving problems. Decide to stop feeding the dry cows (in calf, but not yet calved) their mid-day cake for fear of too big calves. This is not a popular decision and I can hear their reaction while I sit and write.

Alice and Treacle are both strong-willed but forming a strong friendship. How would Alice cope if Treacle had to be destroyed? Read of a tragic story where a farmer's son had hidden his pet lamb in his wardrobe away from the valuer. This disease is tough on farmer's children.

Tuesday 6 March. There are now 72 confirmed cases of foot and mouth disease. We are obsessed with every news report on the radio and television. There are four suspected outbreaks in Somerset still waiting to be confirmed. Dipping our feet and spraying the car is now routine.

This ban on livestock movements to market is taking effect. It costs £10 a week to feed each calf. At present we have 30 calves which is putting our cash flow under tremendous pressure—an extra £300 a week. My fear is that when markets do open again they will be flooded by large numbers of calves which will dramatically reduce the price. The two main calf-sheds are now full and we are cleaning out an old stable to house the next batch of calves. It has no electricity so calf feeding at night in the dark should be an experience.

The cows are now grazing the last field behind the farm. This means we have only ten days of grass before they need to move on. What happens if by then we still cannot take the cows down the lane to another field?

There is good and bad news about our sick cow, No 26. She stood unaided for the first time today once we had lifted her, but tonight she has shuffled her way on to the concrete. She may have damaged her back legs. We won't know until we get her up tomorrow.

Wednesday 7 March. Woke up to chaos this morning. No 11 has worked out she is not with her own calf and in an attempt to find him she smashed down two barriers, broke through into Misty's stable and forced open her stable door. She escaped, followed by her surrogate calves. Misty, in a total state of disbelief, stayed in her open stable all night.

We are feeling trapped and frustrated by the whole situation and it is difficult to make any management plans.

We now have to decide as to whether we want to rent the annual grass keep up on the hill away from the farm. We have to commit ourselves to spending money now, but will we be able to make use of the grass? Will we be able to move any stock on to the land? I have to keep thinking positively that we'll still have cows in the summer.

After an incident on the farm this morning I had to call an ambulance but first I had to clear their entry on to the farm with the switchboard. They were very willing to be sprayed and scrubbed down.

Duncan has only just come in and it is 10 p.m. What a long day. Until the milk price improves it costs us £20 per milking or £40 per day to milk the cows. Usually Duncan is a great positive thinker and constantly reminds us all how lucky we are to live in the countryside but on a bad day, such as today, I can see it really wears him down. A 16-hour day has not earned him any money and this is not good for a man's self-esteem.

How has this situation come about? Why is a litre of milk cheaper than a litre of water? As a result of the Milk Marketing Board and Milk Marque being dissolved by the Mergers and Monopolies Commission the dairy industry has been fragmented into small selling groups.

This has put us at the mercy of a few powerful buyers whose priority is to their shareholders but is currently to the detriment of the primary producer—the British farmer.

They dictate the price we receive but if we are not paid the cost of production the industry will suffer in the long term.

One solution would be to produce from bigger units but we are regulated and government controls do not allows this. We are regulated as to how much milk we can produce, where and which crops we can grow etc. Today we received 16p a litre for our milk and on the supermarket shelves it is 55p a litre (or 31p a pint).

Thursday 8 March. Seventeen new outbreaks announced yesterday, the worst day so far. What does this tell us—has it peaked or is it spreading faster than we all think?

We have received so many letters of support. Phone calls from our local vicar and other churches and a special prayer has been written and distributed around the parish. It would seem that everyone has respected the footpath restrictions. There is a real sense of community.

The blacksmith came today as Misty could wait no longer. We sprayed his truck and as a precaution tied Misty up down the lane. The blacksmith's trade has been severely hit with no hunting or racing.

Fantastic news, No 26 has stood up for the first time on her own. This makes our job so worthwhile when I think of all the hours it has taken.

I am upset by a letter in a newspaper that suggests farmers are shedding crocodile tears over their stock which are being reared for slaughter regardless. Does she really think that we treat a worthless Aberdeen Angus heifer calf (value £1) any differently from a valuable pedigree Friesian heifer calf (value £120). Of course not. All our animals are treated equally.

Friday 9 March. Our fears have been realised. The foot and mouth hotline has declared the first outbreak in Somerset, fifteen miles from us. It has taken ten days for the results to come in. Still no news about the local outbreak at Yarcombe.

How should we react? Should the children have gone to choir practice tonight? Alice sat next to her friend, both farmers' daughters. Just how much should we keep them at home? If need be, Alice could board at school although I think she'd rather have an excuse to stay at home.

If the local outbreak is confirmed all family movements would have to stop but in the meantime surely the children need some normality. Duncan, however, has not left the farm for over two weeks.

The Chief Veterinary Officer has announced that this outbreak will go on for a long time yet. There are a further 20 cases bringing the total to 127.

A sinking feeling has returned and I feel cold as I write this. We almost believed this week that the disease was under some sort of control.

The bank manager says he is now more of a social worker than a banker. He is concerned by the number of farmers unable to sell any stock who are desperately seeking reassurance from the bank. At this stage the bank seems very supportive.

At last No 11 is happy. We have given her back her calf and she is now part of the suckling group of four cows and nine bull calves. All hell is let loose when the cows go in but they all love it. And at least she has stopped mooing.

We took delivery today of some arable sprays which we unloaded at the bottom of the farm drive. Should we in the future be placed under restriction no suppliers will deliver. So we are stocking-up.

Saturday 10 March. Have just applied to MAFF at Bristol for an Occupational Movement Licence. Vital to us so we can continue to graze cows on fresh grass.

MAFF were helpful but as yet they have received no instructions. Hurry up MAFF, we need these licences now.

Watching the tragic stories of the individual farmers on the news is heartbreaking. They all talk about the eerie silence when the slaughter is over. But the animals are not being removed from the farmyards. Haven't the farmers suffered enough without the smell of dead stock constantly reminding them of their personal disaster?

Mr Fox paid us a visit last night. The only victim was William, a Light Sussex cockerel and a family friend. Ironically, we had only just found him a wife, namely Mrs Sussex. The fox will be back. We must be very vigilant.

I drove to Devon this afternoon to collect a tractor wheel rim from a farmer dealing with spare parts. We met at the bottom of the farm drive and his wife declared they were surrounded by farm D cases (dangerous contact category). These could go either way.

Just about to go in tonight when we found two little ginger calves lying deep in the straw. It is vital calves have colostrum (mother's first milk, full of antibodies) within the first eight hours of life. Mum is too proud to stop and feed them. Have to take her in the parlour, milk her out and bottle feed the calves. Missed *Blind Date* but it was worth it.

Sunday 11 March. 137 cases so far. Jim Scudamore admits he is now surprised by the spread of the outbreak.

The concern of the Somerset outbreak is that they cannot link it to any other confirmed case. It may prove to be airborne. The M5 runs alongside the farm, the route of all sheep moved from the northern markets into Devon. If it is airborne the potential spread is devastating.

We have friends in the area whose main farm income is tourism. The Easter trade should bring in hundreds of caravans and holiday makers. However, one Devon caravan park owner declared he had taken one booking and 75 cancellations.

No 26 is very pleased with herself. She can get up and down, eats anything and is slowly bonding with her new calf.

As we are shutting up the cows Duncan points out the wood-cock that flies each evening towards the copse. It is this bird that gave the gun dog, the cocker spaniel, its name.

But we have to hurry indoors to watch the news of the latest outbreaks. Alice says it seems as though foot and mouth has been with us for years. How well children express our thoughts.

Monday 12 March. 174 recorded cases and still rising.

We are shocked by the recent outbreaks in Devon. When we employed college students, they all came from farms in that area. We are so worried for them. Two of our friends have an outbreak on the next-door farm. What a worry. It's only a matter of time, they think.

We have only just received an information pack from the Ministry, two and a half weeks after the first outbreak. This is the first time I have seen pictures of the lesions and blisters.

They look pink, raw and painful. Surely we should have had this information earlier? It is on the Internet but we do not have a computer.

My parents have offered to have both children so they could continue to go to school should we need to shut down the farm totally. As Sam is the lead in the school play, they are anxious he is not kept away.

The race meeting at Taunton has been cancelled and we are

grateful as our fields border their course.

Duncan has just taken a stillborn calf to the hunt kennels. The hunt offers this service even though we've never hunted. Usually they collect fallen stock but, as a precaution, they are asking farmers to take their own calves. Duncan had to ring and book a time so that the car and horsebox could be thoroughly disinfected.

Calves are taking up a big part of my day and it is a juggling act with school runs, children's tea and music lessons. Calves are Jekyll and Hyde animals. For 23 hours a day they are adorable, big-eyed babies. Then twice a day at feeding time they become demented, crazed and able to clear four feet to jump out of their pens. An hour later when all is quiet, I love them again.

Tuesday 13 March. Bill, 80-plus, who worked on the farm for more than 40 years, called in for his milk. He can remember the outbreaks in the 1930s. In those days, outbreaks were more isolated. If a cow and calf were to be sold at Taunton market, he described how one man would halter the calf and walk it three miles to market, the cow quietly following. No lorries driving up the M5 in those days.

Am busy today with paperwork. Paying bills really means deciding which ones we can afford to post. Rent is due in two weeks which will be a struggle as we cannot sell any stock. Perhaps we could pay in calves?

Each week I apply for calf passports for each new-born calf. Everything we do, sell, move, feed, buy in etc is accountable. Everything can be traced back to the source of the farm. But can we trust imported meat in the same way? The EU's official journal last week reported that meat is now being imported from Swaziland even though a limited number of outbreaks of the disease have been recorded on a limited part of its territory. And do they have to fill in calf passports, I wonder?

No 26 has let us down. After all our care, she has shown no maternal instincts towards her adopted calf. By turning around fast on her three good legs, she doesn't give him a chance to feed. We are topping him up but I think No 26 owes us a favour.

Sam helped to feed the calves tonight. I lost my cool with one calf and shouted at Sam. He didn't deserve it but I'm tired and irrational. We made up at bedtime and then Sam said: 'It's all right Mummy, I understand'. That made me feel so guilty.

Wednesday 14 March. Have woken up to the Government declaring this outbreak is now worse that in 1967 and that went on for eight months.

Am ringing the Ministry to request a licence to move the cows on to fresh grazing as they will run out of grass in seven days. They fax their reply. We have asked to move 34 cows 100 yards and have received a 14-page answer. That's almost enough to put us off.

The chairman of the parish council has just rung to ask whether we thought the village spring flower show at the end of the month should be cancelled. On weighing up the risk, we feel it should continue. Are we right? To what lengths should we go to protect our animals?

Late milking tonight as the sucker calves broke out. They couldn't wait for Duncan to open the gates and so they escaped in search of their Mums. When we followed the noise, we found one calf in the parlour, one in the garden, one with the hens and the others scatter-gunned into the herd. They were very strong and hard to catch and not what Duncan wanted before milking.

Suddenly the whole effort of this damn disease is getting to me. I know Duncan and I are under pressure. We haven't had a family day off for weeks or a proper lie in. We seem to take a step forward and two steps backward. Although I must listen to the news, it is depressing me.

Duncan says I mustn't moan but it's a black day today.

Before this outbreak, the milk price was due to rise 1p–2p a litre. So at least we might break even. With the ban on export to the EU, this increase will not happen. And tonight Canada and America declared a total ban on all EU imports. This is now a global problem.

Why have dairy exports been banned when a clear directive from Brussels stated that as long as milk is pasteurised to 72°C for 15 seconds, it could be exported?

Just how long will it take for us to get back to normal? Other countries will take our markets and fight hard to retain them. We couldn't cope if the price of milk or wheat dropped any lower.

Go to bed with a bar of chocolate. I deserve it. The outbreaks have topped 200.

Thursday 15 March. Came downstairs to a quiet kitchen this morning. For the first time since the outbreak, Duncan has not had the radio on.

It seems that he, too, needs a break from the news.

Took time to sit down and read through the Welfare Movement Scheme, particularly the occupational licence.

This section recognises the need to move animals 'from the milking parlour to pasture on a daily basis'! We could apply for the cows to cross the road directly into the field opposite but to move along a road the cows 'must be transported in a suitable vehicle' each time they go out to grass!

How totally impractical. Firstly, we do not own a cattle lorry and, secondly, to load a milking herd into our horsebox one at a time would take all day.

Duncan rang the Ministry to clarify the situation. Rules are rules, we are told. This means we will not be able to graze over 30 acres of grass.

What a sad reflection that Whitehall have behaved like bureaucrats rather than take advice from people who know what is and isn't practically possible.

The BBC are here today filming a documentary addressing the facts behind the foot and mouth outbreak. As a London crew, they were totally supportive and accepted totally only filming in the kitchen or through an upstairs window.

Let's hope their film answers our questions so that we can learn and avoid this dreadful situation ever happening again.

Have just calved a strange little Charolais heifer calf. She is possibly five weeks premature and looks like a skinny rabbit. She is finding it hard to breathe but she is warm and has had colostrum. Nature will decide whether she survives the night. Alice has taken over as chief nurse.

Friday 16 March. News of the proposed mass slaughter is heartbreaking. In theory, it should keep one step ahead of the disease, acting as a fire-break. But what a sacrifice these farmers are making. Sheep farmers will lose at least one year's income. How many will be able to survive that?

Farmers need to be totally reassured that this slaughter is necessary and trust the Government's decision. How could we cope if our healthy stock had to be destroyed.

To add to their frustration, we are still importing unassured meat to stock the supermarket shelves. Four EU countries have brought meat into this country with spinal cord material, which was banned after the BSE crisis.

We are desperate to clean out the sheds as we have had four new cases of mastitis. Although the cows are bedded up daily with fresh straw, the bacteria still breed in these conditions.

Usually we rent a digger from our neighbour but, as he has a beef herd, we are anxious about cross-infection. We dare not employ other contractors as they will have been on other farms in the last six weeks.

Good news. My little rabbit calf has survived the night. Helped her stand and bottle-fed her. She is so tiny but very determined.

Have just rung Brian who will come and clean out one side of the shed this afternoon. His tractor has not been on any other farms. We'll thoroughly spray the tractor and hope that is good enough.

Started to watch *Comic Relief* with the children but as Nick Brown was on *Newsnight*, the children had to turn over. You must know enough about foot and mouth by now, said Alice. If only that were true.

Saturday 17 March. Somerset still only has one confirmed case but a cluster of suspected outbreaks in the area. We are so lucky compared with the Devon farmers, but the dread and fear never leave us. There is always the threat of what tomorrow will bring.

We are trying to keep journeys to a minimum but today I must collect some high-phosphate minerals from the market for the cows. Once calved, the race is on to get back in-calf. No freedom of choice here. High levels of phosphate in the diet promotes oestrus activity.

The plan was to run a bull with the cows from April onwards. But this will not be possible as we are restricted from bringing in any other stock from another holding. Duncan is trained in AI (artificial insemination), having fathered over 900 calves, but we have a better conception rate the 'natural way'.

The longer the outbreak goes on, the more it is affecting our management plan for the dairy herd. At least, thank God, we still have our dairy herd.

Busy day with four calvings. Helped No 74 to calve a magnificent bull calf with the help of a calving aid. There is no way I could have calved her on my own.

No 26 is a total bully and has not accepted the calf. A new approach is needed. Treacle (Alice's calf) is my secret weapon. She is so strong-willed and determined and permanently hungry. If any calf can sort out No 26, she can.

Sunday 18 March. 282 outbreaks now reported. Today we should have gone to an Amway business seminar in Taunton but obviously we do not want to mix with a crowd of people. We have built the business alongside our farming business for over nine years and we always look forward to the positive atmosphere at these meetings.

It has rained continuously for 48 hours and we have decided not to turn the cows out today. Not only is it too wet but we still do not know which field we can graze next. Cows hate a change in routine and they are not happy to be kept in. Lots of verbal resentment and echoes around the yard.

We are still in discussions with the Ministry about the movement licence. The idea of having to use a vehicle to transport a milking herd a hundred yards down the road twice a day is farcical. Although friendly, the officials have no imagination or practical bias towards this problem.

Tomorrow a loved and respected farming neighbour is to be buried. Duncan says that without doubt we shall go to the church but follow strictly all possible precautions. Must ring the vicar about setting up a foot dip.

How can the Ministry say the countryside is open and that it's alright to walk in fields as long as it is not near livestock. All our footpaths across both arable and grassland fields are posted with signs warning of a £5,000 fine for unauthorised access.

The public are receiving mixed messages. Perhaps the Government wants to play down the emergency and assume normality in rural areas.

Monday 19 March. There were 25 cases confirmed yesterday. The total is more than 300. Just statistics—but each one is a farm, a family.

Attended the funeral of a much-loved farmer-contractor who had a reputation for making the sweetest hay in the county. As his doctor said at the funeral, 'When Tommy chose to cut his hay we knew that was the day to have a family barbecue'.

Despite the foot and mouth outbreak there was a large gathering of farmers determined to pay their respects. Had we been in the middle of a local outbreak, whether to attend would have been a difficult decision.

No 26 has met her match in Treacle, who does not give up. We have set up another suckling unit of three cows and six calves, so poor No 26 is outnumbered.

Found our little rabbit calf dead this morning. Sam was quite upset. Her mother, No 42, has a high temperature and I can only assume that the fever caused the premature birth. In the wild this would be called natural selection. A Charolais heifer has jumped in with No 42 and they are bonding well.

Duncan is laying and coppicing an old hedge as part of the countryside stewardship scheme. So as not to disturb nesting birds this has to be done by the end of March. A welcome break from routine.

Tuesday 20 March. Rang MAFF again regarding the Movement Licence. Amazingly, they have had a change of thought and we can walk the cows down the lane rather than use a lorry. Common sense rules. All we need now is for it to stop raining.

Sleet and snow this morning and the cows are hiding behind the barn. Even they do not want to go out.

A farmer rang me from west Somerset to say he had received his licence delivered by hand to his farm. No wonder MAFF say they are busy. I look forward to seeing how ours arrives.

I have received three phone calls from friends all reporting that the Ministry was contacting timber merchants in January about supplies of railway sleepers. They were last contacted in 1967 during that outbreak.

A cow has trodden on No 108's teat and it is a bloody mess. Have strapped it up but it always amazes me how well nature heals. It would be too painful to milk the teat by machine so we will insert a tube which allows the milk to drip out. It seems we've had our fair share of sick animals, but then I remind myself that the vet had not been on the farm for eight months before we started calving.

Emotions are running very high in Cumbria. Why could not more farmers meet Jim Scudamore directly? Farmers are desperate for answers. If someone was going to slaughter our healthy livestock I would want to be told why by the people in charge.

Wednesday 21 March. Another 48 cases yesterday, the worst day so far.

The phone rang at 7.30 a.m. One of our Devon friends has a confirmed foot and mouth outbreak in his heifers—devastating.

Another friend, whose neighbour has a confirmed case, had his pedigree herd destroyed yesterday. When you know the farm and family personally your emotions hit a new level.

Both these farmers are passionate about their cattle and knew their cows' breeding better than their own family trees.

The Government announced that to delay the elections would show the world we are closed for business and send out the wrong signals. Rubbish.

At ground level it's not that complicated. It's simply that Cumbria and Devon are suffering a bereavement and as such need time to mourn in peace.

It cannot be right to start the cull when 80,000 dead stock lie waiting to be moved. When you consider how quickly a dead rabbit is removed by foxes and birds, these carcasses must be considered a risk. Why are not more decisions taken on the farm? Why does everything have to be referred to London?

In our Yellow Pages more than a hundred diggers and earth-movers are listed. This shows the depth of help available locally. Why is it being refused?

The Government must act now and pay the short-term price. If not, we will all be paying in the long term.

Talking to our friends, it is apparent how much they appreciate the care shown by the vets and slaughtermen. Apparently the cows were given a type of sedative so they lay down quietly in the silage pit before slaughter.

Everything was done to consider the welfare of the animals and the farmers. But what effect will it have on these officials surrounded by so much death and despair?

The story of the sleepers has broken on Radio 4 news. What a coincidence after the phone calls I received. The Government deny the link.

In at 8.30 p.m. after another calving and late milking. No time to cook or plan meals so we have devoured most of my mother-in-law's delicious fruitcake. How will I explain that at Slimming World?

Sam has announced he has to make a model of a Tudor house for a school project—due in tomorrow. Quite pleased with the result, so reward myself with another slice of fruitcake.

On *Newsnight* a leading epidemiologist predicted the outbreak would go on for another six months and has still not peaked. Figures show that the outbreak will peak in early May. That will be interesting.

Totally depressing, so Duncan and I finish the fruitcake.

Thursday 22 March. There are 435 cases—new cases are now 40-plus a day. We used to think 20 was a lot.

Return from the school run to find the postman has delivered the post to the back door. Must ring the Post Office and renew the warning signs. We must not become complacent about our procedures.

I chatted to a farmer this morning in the village shop, who was totally unaware of the movement licences available. Understandably, he had been concerned about how he would turn his cows out to grass. Why have we not received any communication from MAFF regarding licence details? We have friends who did not know they were in the exclusion zone until they found themselves listed on the Internet. Please listen, MAFF, we need to be kept in touch.

Taunton Racecourse has changed its policy and decided to hold a meeting next week. In their defence they are digging out vehicle dips and will block off the lane to keep vehicles away from the farm.

Many race supporters come up from Devon and our farm is only a field away. How can we quantify the risk? To us it's a worry and not what we want.

There are some foot and mouth stories that make me smile, such as a friend telling me of a family who have set up their car port as a makeshift lambing shed for a flock stranded away from home. But for many it is taking far too long for movement licences to be issued. Animals are suffering because of it. Saw tragic pictures on the news of new-born lambs drowned at birth. The flock was stranded on the Somerset Levels. How can we justify this level of suffering. Cut red tape, MAFF, and allow these animals home.

Friday 23 March. As we are spending so little time with the children we have taken them into town this afternoon for shopping and tea. Obviously the excitement of getting away from the farm affected Duncan and me. Alice and Sam declared we were behaving like toddlers, causing them total embarrassment and they walked ten paces in front of us.

We were persuaded to dine at McDonald's. Another embarrassing situation when we quizzed the manager about the source of his beef while a long queue built up behind us. We chose fish and chicken.

What news we come back to. The Chief Scientific Officer has declared the disease out of control. He predicts more than 4,000 cases by June.

All day farmers have received conflicting news of the proposed cull. This is playing with farmers' emotions. A total disgrace. Get your act together, MAFF.

The scientists have given the Government an ultimatum: reduce the time from identification to slaughter and disposal to 24 hours and we will see a dramatic reduction of outbreaks. Have you got what it takes, Mr Brown?

The news has totally upset Duncan. He's deeply angry. So angry at the lack of urgency in controlling this disease. They missed a chance, he says.

Just when we didn't need it we have another cow gone down, in the dirtiest part of the yard of course. I can see Duncan is totally worn out. I rely on him so much and find it hard to cope when he is like this. A virus out of control is very frightening.

We lift No 52 up in the net, as ironically No 26 looks on. Finally we feed and settle her down and go in to watch the news.

Saturday 24 March. With 54 new cases the total is over 500. What a watershed. I have just asked Duncan to milk record the cows this morning. 'No', he snapped. 'I'm sorry, I can't cope with anything extra today. It's all too depressing. Damn them all.'

Duncan is starting his 12-hour day angry and frustrated. This must be the picture on the majority of farms all over the country.

A cow has just calved down in the bottom shed and needs to come up to the yard with her calf. I loaded the still-wet calf into the wheel barrow. 'Run', shouts Duncan, as he tries to keep the other cows back and encourage Mum to follow me.

'Run' and me are not words that go together. Going through a giant puddle I discover I have a hole in my wellie. No sympathy from husband, who is still shouting, 'Faster, faster'.

A woman from the Ministry rang regarding a query on our licence application. I asked about morale in the local offices. The staff are quite upset by all the media criticism, but when I suggested the problems came from a higher level she answered: 'No comment'. She was just finishing a 12-hour shift.

No 52 is eating well but is unable to get up. The vet suggests as long as she is fully dilated we calve her.

Twins. Two adorable tiny Charolais heifers. Duncan has quite a job sorting out which feet belonged to which calf. The second calf had her head doubled back and Duncan, having stripped off, was lying flat out on the straw pushing the front legs back in to release the head. As we pulled her out she never took her eyes off Duncan. It was quite amazing.

Finally, at 10 p.m., we left a very proud but exhausted mother. Five healthy calves and four healthy mothers today, so that balanced the score a little.

Sunday 25 March. A sense of urgency has arrived in Cumbria. The Army are out in full force and setting up facilities to dispose of half a million sheep. What a relief for the community. Just writing 'half a million sheep' reminds me of the sheer scale of this outbreak.

Mother's Day and I have received two lovely handmade cards. The time and effort it took means so much to me.

I was too busy to go to the Mothering Sunday service. The first one I have missed in twelve years. Work and family time is out of balance, so next week we'll plan for some help on Sunday. I've been saying too often, 'Not now, darling' or 'When I've finished outside I'll play with you'.

The cows were desperate to go out to grass. It is a dry day but too muddy underfoot. The solution will be to lay cow tracks through the fields, but that would be a major investment. Possibly worth it though, as the milk has dropped back since we've had to keep them in.

No 108's teat is healing well. We re-dress it every few days and she seems to be in no pain. The disfigured shape of the teat will not enhance her good looks for the bull but at her age I don't think she'll mind.

Duncan and our neighbours have written to the clerk of the course at Taunton as we feel the proposed meeting is extremely inconsiderate to the farming community. We await their reply.

On a lighter note, Alice, who is due to go on a school French exchange in May, is upset. Because of the restrictions she and her friends cannot take any sweets or chocolate on the journey.

It seems that foot and mouth affects us all in many different ways.

Monday 26 March. 52 new cases. Total outbreaks more than 600. Still more than 250,000 animals to cull and 118,000 for disposal. This virus is running ahead of the cull.

As my Mother's Day present, the children fed the calves last night so I could be in early and relax in the bath, so I feel better today.

When will it stop raining? At least some spring sunshine would give us hope. The cows are back inside full time on full winter rations. Each year we have to calculate our winter feed stocks and by good housekeeping ensure we have enough until spring. But when does spring arrive, is the dilemma.

The news pictures are horrific. But at least the Army is allowed to do a professional job in Cumbria. It is still a shock to see lorryloads of dead sheep being brought into the trenches. Each carcass represents an animal carefully reared by local farmers.

It is an obscene sight. If MAFF had tackled the outbreak with more speed and efficiency in those early days just think how many sheep could have been saved.

Tuesday 27 March. We found No 52 dead this morning. She had been losing weight before calving and the vet suggested some other cause of death, such as a diseased liver. The sight of a dead cow is still a shock. How are farmers coping with a yard full of dead cows? Nothing could prepare you for it.

The hunt are unable to collect cows as their lorry has broken down and I rang a local abattoir for a quote—it was £58 to take her away. We receive nothing back even though the meat is used for pet food.

Busy afternoon cleaning out another cow shed, so distracted from making a decision. From the news it would seem that the foot and mouth virus came into this country on imported meat, legal or otherwise. For the sake of all the animals slaughtered and the farming and tourist livelihoods destroyed, this government must control the importation of illegal meat.

On 3 March 2001, two weeks after the first outbreak, baggage handlers at Heathrow refused to handle bags leaking blood and covered in maggots arriving from Ghana. The bags were found later, but the contents had disappeared. Heathrow officials were prepared to admit they are set up for drug control but have no procedures in place to control illegal meat imports. In December last year fifteen dead monkeys, declared as vegetables, brought in the terrifying risk of human disease, notably Ebola. Why can't we learn from other countries? A friend today rang from New Zealand. They are terrified of diseases coming in on meat and fruit. Airline passengers have to fill in paperwork making them aware of import requirements and bins are provided to throw in any fruit products.

As in Australia and America, agricultural enforcement officials walk alone along the lines of passengers, accompanied by trained sniffer dogs. Duncan's cousin returned from a day trip on Eurostar today. At no point were any foot and mouth restrictions made clear or any type of disinfecting area visible. He could easily have travelled from a farming community in Essex or Kent. In fact, he lives in London.

Wednesday 28 March. Now 728 cases. Rang the abattoir to take the cow away. Our indecision has cost us an extra £10 as the carcass is a day older. Then they ran back to say they wouldn't take the cow at all as she is not 'fresh'. We take advice, find a digger driver and bury her on the farm.

Mike came back to work today to discover we now have 52 baby calves to feed. His first job is to feed five three-day-old calves running together in one pen. Calves have not heard of taking turns and see Mike only as a milk-machine. No wonder, after being sucked, dribbled on and butted in places that hurt, we could hear Mike loudly questioning their parentage from over the stable door. Number one job this afternoon is to clean out the old workshop and pen the calves individually.

Surprised to receive a call from the Ministry regarding our licence to move the milkers on to fresh grass. Not only did they mislay our faxed application twice, but having given us a verbal agreement they are now backtracking.

They suggest 100 metres is too far to take cows along a lane. Apparently we must disinfect the road in front of and behind the cows. No problem, we suggest, with a knapsack sprayer. Whitehall is being asked. I wonder whether any Whitehall official has ever used a knapsack sprayer. Yet their decisions affect our profitability.

Thursday 29 March. More than 750 cases confirmed. New outbreak in South Devon causes worry, as there is no link with other cases in Devon.

Cleaning out the sheds has helped the mastitis problem. Turning out full time would completely cure it.

We start serving in April and will have to make a decision regarding the choice of bull. Charolais calves usually fetch a good market price but are born a week later, possibly producing bigger calves. Out of 55 calvings this year we have only lost three calves, but four cows have endured hard calvings and will not produce much milk this lactation. Is this too high a price to pay?

The calves, who look wonderful, would probably average £100 per head. That's a lot of money tied up when they are on the cash flow under 'sales'. Who can guess at the trade when the markets open up?

We only have one shed left which we can use for calves. Duncan is threatening to use Misty's stable, much to Alice's annoyance. Will be interesting to see who wins this battle.

The children are so excited as friends are passing us on their three-year-old computer. The Internet carries so much more information regarding the outbreak than we receive in the post.

Bought a new pair of wellies. Opted for the cheaper pair. False economy? Duncan's logic is that when you stick a fork in your wellie it makes the same hole, whatever the price.

Why can't we have a decision on the election? Let's stop speculation and ask the Government to put 100 per cent of its energies into solving this crisis.

After this morning's rain we've enjoyed the warmest sunshine this year. This'll make the grass grow.

Friday 30 March. Duncan rushes in for the hacksaw. Two heifers are stuck in the pit in the parlour (where we stand and they shouldn't). At least our problems have variety.

Some of our creditors are keen to be paid. Having moved the herd to spring calving we knew we would not have a milk cheque between January and March but had budgeted to sell calves during that period.

'Survivor' is causing problems. Born two months premature he somehow survived and has grown into a one-year-old Belgian Blue runt. His size means he can squeeze through most gaps and having tasted sweet grass he escapes every day. This drives Duncan wild. He wishes the market would open up just to sell 'Survivor'. The children, of course, think he's wonderful. (That's 'Survivor', not Duncan.)

Good to read that Waitrose will continue paying its British farmers the same or a higher price for meat during the foot and mouth crisis. They will absorb the extra costs of slaughtering home-reared beef cattle. It cannot be right that the farmer is receiving less for his beef and lamb than before the outbreak. Surely meat of such assured quality should deserve a premium.

Rang the Ministry again, reference the licence. London reports no relaxation on the rules.

The official report after the 1967 outbreak highlighted the problem when cows and beef cattle were turned out. Many farms will be running out of winter feed and cattle may have to share pastures with sheep. Once out cattle will be more vulnerable.

Saturday 31 March. Now 818 cases—more than twenty cases in five days.

Today is the village spring flower show. The kitchen is in chaos. Alice and Sam are making their 'Gardens on a plate', the flapjacks are cooking in the Aga and I'm madly picking daffodils.

Today the weekly lab test shows our cell counts (indicating the underlying level of mastitis) are high. We suspect it must be due to one or two cows with a high count. We are grateful to the local National Milk Records field manager, who delivers the sample bottles for this afternoon's milking. From the results, we'll be able to identify the problem cows and treat them accordingly.

After prize-giving at the show it's back to reality and the work still has to be done. When Duncan and I came in tonight after 9 p.m., feeling down and tired, what message are we giving to the children. Where will the next generation of farmers come from when our children are not picking up any positive signals about farming?

April

Sunday 1 April. Our first lie-in for seven weeks. The world seems to a better place today.

The election is to be postponed. Thank goodness for a decision. An election would only have distracted the Government which should be devoting all its time to sorting out the foot and mouth crisis. The figures speak for themselves. This week the waiting list for animals to be slaughtered has doubled to over 300,000. Consider this when the daily slaughter rate is only 40,000 animals. Action is needed to remedy this ratio. Each day's delay means more animals are slaughtered and businesses destroyed unnecessarily.

Even after five weeks we still tune into every news and my heart still stops whilst they declare the new outbreaks. That feeling of dread never leaves us. We live with a continual creeping anxiety.

Spoke to the Ministry at Bristol again. We have now been issued with four licences. It seems all our 'lost' faxed copies were discovered later and each one treated as a new application.

The weatherman promised us spring this afternoon before the rain returns tomorrow. The cows are confused and hang their heads over the gate desperate to go out. Usually one moos, which sets the whole herd into a choral moo of disgust.

Monday 2 April. They promised us rain and we've got it. Amazing that in only a few hours the chicken paddock is once again reminiscent of the Somme, whereas yesterday the chickens were enjoying dust baths in the afternoon sun.

Misjudged how long it would take to feed the 52 calves this morning, so Sam was late for the technical rehearsal of the school production of *Joseph*. As he is the lead, this caused temporary panic among the staff.

The election has been postponed, quite rightly, as the country is clearly involved in a crisis that demands 100 per cent of its time and effort.

Read in the *Telegraph Travel* an account of a family holiday on a farm in Devon—offering 'real' farm holidays. The writer described his holiday as taking part in a 'real life drama'. As this farm is in deepest Devon and the article was printed only two days before the first outbreak, I can imagine their new scale of real life drama.

Tuesday 3 April. Surprise outbreak at a Bristol city farm. MAFF confirms this to be a wind-borne infection. That is very frightening and makes me feel quite powerless.

Today, the news talks of the outbreak being under control. Worried that foot and mouth may be becoming old news. People are expressing cautious optimism. I appreciate the public may have a limit on how many times they can cope with pictures of burning pyres, but we need public support until the very last case. The evidence of 1967 shows we must not become complacent.

Duncan discovered a heifer, No 4, freshly calved lying flat out, seemingly trapped in a slight depression in the straw. How he ever manages to turn a cow right over when she weighs 450 kg amazes me. As she seemed unwilling to get up, Duncan drenched her with a new homeopathic treatment. Five minutes later she stood up. Coincidence or not?

Great news. We have been granted our occupational licence. Surely it makes sense to let local officials make local decisions.

Duncan and I were still milking and feeding calves at 10 p.m. tonight. Although tired, I felt quite high having had a day away from the farm helping with the dress rehearsal of *Joseph*.

Wednesday 4 April. 48 new cases. Twice as many as yesterday. Not a reason to be cautiously optimistic, I think.

The bank rang to ask if we needed to extend our borrowing facility. How easy to say yes. How difficult ever to pay it back. But with no calf sales and extra rearing costs, my figures suggest we will need that facility. This news will really knock Duncan. But I must find the right time to tell him, and that's not 10 o'clock at night when he's knackered.

When the milk price dropped by 5p per litre, it erased £22,500 from our profit. Before foot and mouth we confidently expected a 2p per litre rise. Now that the global effect of this disease has damaged exports, will we see that price rise?

Taunton Races, due to run tomorrow, have been cancelled. What a great relief. The officials felt that whatever precautions they took, someone would come from an infected area.

The parish council would like to open up some of the footpaths across the farm. How do we feel about that? The footpaths only cross arable land, well away from the cows. It would seem common sense to open the access, but how can we measure the risk?

Thursday 5 April. Mixed signals. The disease has produced the 1,000th outbreak on a farm in Devon. The Chief Scientific Officer suggests his prediction of 4,000 cases by June may have been too high. What are we to think?

The cows have gone out today, the first time for over two weeks. Because the rain was so heavy they couldn't believe anyone would be mad enough to turn them out, so I found them all tucked up in the barn. One loud shout of 'Come on girls' and 50 ladies rushed for the gate.

Duncan sprayed the road using the knapsack sprayer as the conditions of the licence require us to clean and disinfect the lane before and after the cows. We must clean up any dung and keep cars back whilst the cows walk along the lane.

We have had to call the vet out for the first time this season for No 42, the mother of the little calf. Wherever possible we have avoided having the vet because of the risk involved. The cow looks very sick, will not eat or drink, and chooses to lie down all day. The vet diagnoses a type of twisted gut and pericardial infection. The choice was to either put her down or give her a chance with drugs.

Steve Glas, our vet, is under extreme pressure with the sheer volume of work. One of the vets from his practice has gone to Devon to help as a temporary Ministry vet. But the administrative work demanded by the movement licence applications in the practice means he will have to be recalled. Is this situation being repeated by other vet practices all over the country? If so, are other vets lined up to take over? If the 24 hours to slaughter policy is to be carried out, are there enough vets on the ground? This Somerset vet has proved very popular in Devon. Through no fault of their own, foreign vets who do not speak English cannot offer the same type of support.

We enjoyed a brilliant last night of *Joseph* and we were very proud of Sam. When a camel appeared on stage, I did wonder if anyone had applied for a licence or dipped his feet.

Friday 6 April. Quite amazing. No 42 is like a different cow. The muscle relaxant and antibodies have worked wonders and she has gone out to grass and is eating well. Thank goodness we took the risk to have the vet and invested in her treatment.

Letter from Alice's school starts: 'On the advice from the French Ministry of Education, the school exchange with England will not take place due to the foot and mouth outbreak'.

The farm in Cornwall where I was a farm student is in trouble. They run a tourist attraction built around a working dairy farm. Having invested over £100,000 in improvements they are now losing over £3,000 per week while closed. What despair for the tourist industry.

After having spoken to Steve the vet yesterday, Duncan and I were both anxious about the vets helping out in infected areas, but coming back on to our farm. Glad to receive their newsletter that reassured us that the vet will not do any farm work for three days after working for MAFF, the official quarantine period. Any car used in Devon is thoroughly steam cleaned and disinfected before coming back on to farms in Somerset.

Busy time as seven calvings in 36 hours. Looking back through the records, this coincides with the change of bull nine months ago. We laughed as we remembered the image of pushing the first bull back into the lorry exhausted and weak kneed after his intimate liaisons with 50 wives. The new bull, in contrast, pushed his way down the ramp and ran across the field looking forward to saying hello. Now, where do we put seven new calves?

Saturday 7 April. Total cases 1,084. Why am I still reading of inefficiencies and lack of resources? Why did MAFF not follow the conclusions of an Army report after 1967 which said they should be brought in immediately?

To compound the situation is the number of animals registered into the voluntary welfare disposal scheme. Intervention Board figures show 1,432,509 animals are registered. There is a theoretical capacity, with 19 different abattoirs involved, to slaughter the equivalent of 280,000 sheep per week. So far, only 17,000 animals have been slaughtered each week. Some animals are suffering in appalling conditions. We need the welfare scheme to work.

Easter holidays start today. At least that means I can feed the calves in peace in the morning without having to clock-watch and make packed lunches.

It seems we must apply for new licences. Here we go again. We need a licence to move a bull into the herd at serving time and a licence to move the young stock out to grass. From our experiences, the sooner we do this the better. A local movement licence is more complicated and the stock must be inspected by MAFF and the vet. More expense, but I do appreciate the need for such control.

Sunday 8 April. Shocking news. The second outbreak in three days to have jumped the fire-break. The farm at Whitby is 40 miles from the nearest case.

I always suspected the virus might creep towards us, but a 40-mile jump shows how vulnerable we all still are. To the north, the disease is 15 miles away and to the south it's 25 miles. Our future depends on the wind direction, it seems.

A glider pilot described how, at cloud level, he is often circled by burning straws, paper, cardboard and ash. How can we measure the level of contamination in the ash from the pyres? And we have no control over where this contamination might land.

I feel the next week will be crucial. Are those two farms isolated wind-borne cases or is this to be the pattern of spread?

On a good note, No 42 led the herd out to grass this morning. She deserved that second chance.

Monday 9 April. The swallows have arrived. As we let the cows into the field today two birds skimmed the grass, feeding. I have such admiration for these little birds when I consider the enormous distance they have flown.

For the second day running Treacle, Alice's calf, has escaped under the gate and spent all night gorging herself on the suckler cows. This morning she is regretting her greed and looks very sorry for herself. The suckled calves are looking magnificent. Who can say what price they will make? Will the markets be flooded when trading eventually starts?

Taunton market usually sells more than 500 calves each week. This suggests there must be in excess of 4,000 calves on local farms all facing an uncertain future.

The census lady called today. It seems her brief is to call personally door-to-door at each address. Is this happening in foot and mouth restricted areas? Why not use the post for all farm addresses?

Tuesday 10 April. More than 1,150 confirmed cases. Why is it becoming harder to find the figures relating to the number of animals awaiting slaughter and disposal? I'm in no doubt it's because the Ministry cannot keep up and the numbers just keep growing.

All farmers have received a letter from Nick Brown asking for their full cooperation with the culling policy.

The sheer scale of this policy is illustrated by the mention of the burial pit at Great Orton. It is the size of 64 football pitches. I can't imaging 64 football pitches let alone imagine the numbers of animals that it will take to fill that pit.

The letter also reports on the plan to keep cattle housed longer and ensure they do not graze with sheep. The majority of farmers are running out of winter feed and turning out is a necessity but thank goodness we have enough feed. Apparently farmers can only apply for aid to buy in extra feed.

I saw one desperate farmer on television who rang the helpline to explain she was keeping her sheep in to reduce the risk of infection but only had one day's hay left and could they help?

They suggested she might like to slaughter them under the voluntary welfare scheme to solve her problem. I think they missed the point.

Wednesday 11 April. With ten calves now born recently, calf housing is now becoming a challenge. Duncan is threatening to use Misty's stable and for the calves to set up squatters' rights.

Alice says he wouldn't dare. We shall see.

We have one last shed to clean out. This shed is equivalent to a suburban attic and has housed all the rubbish for the past 20 years.

Sam has discovered Easter chicks. He heard chicks cheeping in the calf-shed and found eleven bantam chicks in an old feed hopper. Catching Mum as well was quite a problem, but finally we settled them all in a rabbit hutch for safety.

A little speckled chick was cold and not well. Sam wrapped it up and took it to the Aga to warm up. Discovering he had placed it in the bottom oven, I quickly asked if he had shut the door. 'Yes', he said.

A mad dash into the kitchen rescued the chick before any damage was done.

Although the racecourse has cancelled the race meeting, car boot sales will take place on the site every Sunday, starting Easter Sunday. Are we worried about this? The cars will pass through a specially prepared wheel bath as they go in and out of the site. Hopefully the event will only attract local people rather than from Devon. We will have to wait and see.

Thursday 12 April. The M5 was very busy. I was struck by the number of lorries moving straw into the South West to fuel new pyres. On a more positive note, the holiday traffic was heavy.

Devastated tonight to learn of a confirmed outbreak at Membury, just over the hill. The news hit us like a bullet. It's all very well hearing that the disease may have peaked but when a new outbreak is only ten miles away statistics are irrelevant.

Duncan and I got out the map and measured the distance between us and the outbreak. I rang the foot and mouth helpline, who confirmed the restricted area is a 10 km radius from the infected site. The infected farm has 2,000 animals.

An immediate worry is that in a restricted area we would not be able to bring in any semen to serve the cows. It is crucial for us to be able to get the cows back in calf.

Rumours are flying but it seems the disease may have come in with a local who has been working in infected areas of Devon. If this is confirmed it shows how careful everyone must be.

Friday 13 April. The local outbreak has unnerved us all. Is this going to be an isolated outbreak or has it already started to spread?

For the slaughter policy to be successful the animals on the infected farm must be slaughtered within 24 hours and the contact farms within 48 hours. Apparently fifteen farms surrounding Membury are to have all their stock slaughtered.

MAFF in Devon confirms they are virtually keeping up with the 24-hour target but are nowhere near the 48-hour deadline of the ring cull. The sheer numbers are breaking the system. If our healthy stock had to be slaughtered as part of this ring cull, the supposed long-term control of this disease, I would be angry and devastated if targets were not met and they were slain in vain.

Why are these bottlenecks happening? Are we still short of slaughtermen? Is too much time spent valuing individual animals? Are we still short of vets on the ground? It is worth noting that France, two or three times larger than the UK, has a state veterinary service with over 3,000 vets, whereas the number in this country has been cut to only 200.

If these targets are not being met do we have to rethink the whole process? Should vaccination be plan B? As a layman I am confused by the conflicting articles I read, for and against vaccination. Yes, vaccination would in the short term severely affect exports, but an ineffective slaughter policy will also delay a return to normal trading. My concern is how to identify carriers after vaccination. A vaccinated animal can still become infected, carrying the virus in its pharynx in the throat without developing characteristic blisters. These animals then become carriers, sheep for up to nine months and cows for as long as three years.

Saturday 14 April. Now 1,280 infected cases. Have just read a fascinating article on foot and mouth published in *Armchair Science* printed in 1935. Other than the photographs of traditional short-horn cows it could have been printed this year.

Even the scene of the outbreak was linked to infected wrappers used on imported meat and offal. Have we really learnt so little about the disease in 66 years? However, the cost to the country in compensation for slaughtered stock was only £30,000. Today we are talking in billions of pounds.

A calf has gone missing. We had to bring up three cows and calves from the bottom shed but could only find two calves. We have searched for more than an hour but have found nothing. In the wild, calves hide all day away from predators and come out only to be fed.

Busy day cleaning out the old workshop. Duncan uncovered the old loader and fork for the scraper tractor amongst the nettles to speed things up.

Taunton Agricultural Show has just been cancelled. Although a young show it is always a popular day out. The decision to cancel has thrown the whole future of the show into doubt.

Very late milking as we achieved our goal and finished the shed. No electricity so feeding by torchlight should be fun. I tucked up the children in bed and went out to help Duncan. Our strength is our ability to support each other but when you're tired and anxious it takes a lot of effort.

Sunday 15 April. Easter Sunday. My favourite day as I can eat chocolate without a conscience. The children have gone to Easter Service but yet again the sheer amount of work means Duncan and I are too busy to go. Still no calf. We have searched again but no luck. I shall be worried if we do not find him by tonight as he'll be hungry.

It is so frustrating being unable to get an update of the news until evening. We are in contact with local farmers but we have so little accurate information. Lots of rumours, but we need the facts.

Monday 16 April. Latest total is 1,323 confirmed cases.

The missing calf has returned. He came out of hiding on Sunday evening, calling loudly for his supper. He was so hungry it was tempting to give him double rations but Mum hasn't given him a second thought and has settled back into the herd.

Drama at milking this morning as No 108 (the cow who cut her teat) walked in, blood pouring from a deep cut in her udder. How frightening blood can be when it pumps out. I suddenly remembered how, as a student, we would stem the flow of blood when castrating piglets—cobwebs.

Duncan collected a handful from the ceiling and I pushed the cobwebs into the wound and applied pressure with a wad of paper towel. The blood stopped pumping, slowly seeped and finally stopped. I think cobwebs produce a unique clotting process—whatever, it worked.

It is obvious that agricultural traders are being hit by foot and mouth, too. We have received a letter encouraging us to buy wormers for our cattle, but now offering a 100 per cent refund if our stock are to be slaughtered in the future. What a unique guarantee.

Even most grazing agreements are incorporating a clause with a pro rata payment should the stock be affected by foot and mouth.

Tuesday 17 April. The race is on to get the cows back in calf. We usually hire an Aberdeen Angus bull for the heifers, first time-calvers, as he produces a small calf. Restrictions are making it difficult to get a bull on to our holding. Although we can artificially inseminate, it relies on spotting a heifer bulling (on heat). In our experience the natural way is the best way. Some things never change.

Have just applied tail-paint on to the cows which acts as a heat detector. The choice is pink or blue. Does the colour of the paint determine the sex of the calf, asked the man in the shop? If only it were that easy.

A six-week-old Charolais heifer is scouring badly and being bullied by her peers. The children helped me clean out a pen and move the calf. Rather than pay weekly pocket money we pay the children for the jobs they do around the farm. Alice is a spender but Sam a careful saver.

Wednesday 18 April. A day off. I had been invited to a very smart lunch in a very smart restaurant in London to join a group of distinguished guests to discuss how foot and mouth and the BSE crisis have affected our views on food, from production through to consumption.

For me, it confirmed what a divide there is between town and country lifestyles. For example, I was told that flats are being designed in London without a real kitchen as people choose to eat out. A fridge and a microwave is all clients ask for.

A question was raised around the table as to the date of harvest time. Only two people knew the date corn is harvested, which confirmed to me the gap between the urban and rural dweller. But surely there is a mutual benefit for us to understand each other's way of life. As a farmer, I must understand the need of a consumer in order to sell my product.

As a country girl at heart, I was quite proud that I scrubbed up quite well and coped with finding my way around in London. I could understand that travelling home on the Tube and train after a hard day's work must be exhausting. Duncan always says how lucky he is to be able to walk to work.

It was a thrill for a day but I was very pleased to return home. Duncan had only just finished milking and Alice had fed the calves for me. Thank you.

Thursday 19 April. Confirmed cases at 1,385.

The number of new outbreaks does seem to be falling, but nearly a million animals are awaiting disposal or slaughter.

The farmer's wife from the local outbreak at Membury has rung me. My heart goes out to her and her family as from talking to her it seems nothing can prepare you for the distress and devastation caused by an outbreak.

The actual cull took more than two and a half days to complete and at the time of writing the animals are still lying around the farm. Dead sheep lie adjacent to the village school with children due back next week. Apparently the NFU have been brilliant and the village has offered real support.

The source of the outbreak is still unknown and our conversation has made me aware of how much distress rumours can cause. But with farmers feeling such isolation on their farms, rumours are often spread by fear and anxiety.

Vaccination? People ask me whether we support the idea. On a personal level my questions would be how long would our vaccinated herd be allowed to live and who would buy our milk and meat? I rang Milk Link (our milk buyers) this morning to ask whether they would continue to collect milk from vaccinated herds. They are still waiting for clear Ministry recommendations but are aware that for vaccination to work the milk would have to be pasteurised outside the infected zone. With the threat of no milk income, I'm not sure any dairy farmer would accept vaccination.

Why are we being told there will be a ban on exports and live animals if we vaccinate? During the 1980s we continued to import meat and breeding stock from countries within the EEC who were part of a compulsory policy of vaccination. Is this a case of double standards?

A Charolais heifer is very sick tonight and Sam has sat with her for the past hour. I cannot stop her scouring. She is lying flat out breathing very fast. Duncan has given her two different homeopathic treatments so we must wait and see.

Friday 20 April. Amazing, the Charolais heifer is alive. I have to admit that I did not think she would survive the night. Was it the homeopathic treatment or the antibiotics?

Have moved the cows back into the Italian Rye Grass as the field has dried up. Unfortunately this early grass has become rather coarse and long. Ideally, it should have been eaten off three weeks ago had the weather allowed.

The milk cheque arrived today. Our first cheque for three months. Unfortunately, the high cell count has cost us £800. The situation is now under control but this was a costly mistake. The combination of the foot and mouth crisis and the sheer number of cows calving distracted us. The only good news is that it won't happen again.

The first race meeting since the outbreak has been held at Taunton today. Our lane was closed off to all traffic to reduce the risk.

How interesting that they are marching in Holland tomorrow to protest against the slaughter of healthy cattle. All Dutch cattle vaccinated against foot and mouth are to be slaughtered within two months of being injected. It questions why the welfare groups have been so quiet in this country.

Saturday 21 April. It is now two months since the first outbreak.

How do we feel as a family two months on? Every day we thank God we have escaped this disease but my heart aches for all the innocent animals slaughtered. We are more stressed, our work-load is greater and our bank balance is poorer. But we know we are a lot better off than many families.

The Government is keen to say that the disease is now 'under control'. Why do I feel there is a hidden agenda in this headline? I think they are desperate to draw a line under the foot and mouth crisis and move on to the election. The Government has forced a timetable that requires foot and mouth to be sorted our by 7 June.

But here in the country it's not as simple as that. Devon has nearly 200,000 carcasses waiting for disposal. Apparently its new burial pit will not be ready for two weeks. I can imagine how decomposed the bodies will be by then. At Membury, the disease-free cattle have been moved before the infected sheep. Surely this is illogical. I think when the stock has gone and farmers have no animals to look after will be the hardest times. A nursing friend working in a general practice in Devon says they have been given list of farmers who are considered 'at risk' with high stress levels. They are being asked to keep a special eye on these families.

Spoke to a Ministry vet in Exeter today who confirms the weather is a major contributor in controlling this disease. The recent dry weather and higher levels of UV light have done much to control the spread this week.

Sunday 22 April. Duncan has had enough of the winter routine and turned the cows out full time last night. This should save three hours' work a day. We have woken up to heavy rain. Will it be too wet to keep them out tonight?

A three-week-old calf, desperate to find Mum, has just got the better of three men who have chased her around the yard for the last half-hour. Mum and calf are now reunited.

Cleaned the yard and removed the old straw dip this morning. Suddenly we were aware of how ineffective this had become, being wet and muddy. Laid down new straw and soaked it in disinfectant. We will not let up on the precautions. It is too easy to think it won't be us.

Having asked a friend how she is coping, she simply said: 'All we can do is pray and spray'.

Monday 23 April. There are now over 1,450 confirmed cases.

Sam went back to school today so the morning routine is chaotic once again. The older calves are quick to feed but it still takes fourteen trips, carrying four heavy buckets at a time. I'm sure my arms are getting longer.

Spoke to a neighbour's son who has been involved in the burning and is now cleaning up infected farms. Farmers have a choice as to whether they clean up themselves and get paid well, quite rightly, or call in the MAFF team. The logistics of arranging diggers, dumper trucks, washers and labour are incredible.

It is taking over two weeks with a team of ten people to clean some individual farms. They are scraping muck and straw out of crevices and cracks with a penknife as the virus can survive in muck.

An ex-farm student of ours from Devon, whose stock was slaughtered a few weeks ago, has chosen to clean up the farm himself. Keeping busy is vital when your barns and milking parlours are empty. Any tools or machinery needed are immediately available, and the MAFF inspection at the end is meticulous.

Tuesday 24 April. Received the booklet *Vaccination: The Facts* from MAFF this morning, which answers the questions raised by the NFU on the possible use of vaccination. Interesting reading, but this is week nine of the outbreak. Why were these questions not asked and answered weeks ago?

Travelled up the M5 to take Sam to the dentist between Taunton and Weston-super-Mare, a distance of perhaps 30 miles. I only saw one dairy herd out at grass. Usually I would see 15–20. I wonder how much longer winter feed stocks will last?

Rang the council as I read in the local paper of the offer of rate relief for businesses suffering due to the foot and mouth outbreak. Apparently as we pay council tax and not business rates we are not eligible but could claim for housing benefit. It's worth a try.

It's baby rabbit season. Tabitha, No 1 cat, struggled into the yard carrying one. As Sam shouted, Tabitha dropped her prey. It died from shock, as they always do, but it doesn't stop Sam from trying to save them.

Wednesday 25 April. The daily number of cases is dropping, thank goodness, but the misery in Devon is relentless. Over 120,000 carcasses are still awaiting disposal and friends say you cannot get away from the smell, which hangs in the air.

Duncan and the crop consultant have walked the arable fields this afternoon. Considering the weather and the very heavy ground the wheat and beans look better than we could have hoped. Duncan deserved some good news. However, they only predict 70 per cent of the usual harvest.

What awful weather. Did I miss spring? The heavy rain means the cows are being yo-yoed in and out at night. One night in, one night out. To produce a good milk yield cows need a routine in their diet.

I finished off the milking tonight in lovely evening sunshine. Seventy cows were pushing against the gates, quite unaware that their feet would damage the pasture if they went out. All they could feel was the sun on their backs. I drove them back into the barn but they were very unsettled.

Duncan is out tonight so I kept checking for a break-out. Cows always announce a break-out by mooing loudly and don't realise that if only they escaped quietly they'd probably get away with it.

Thursday 26 April. Good news. The farmers' market in Taunton is open today and meat is once again on sale. These markets are a lifeline for local producers. One stallholder, Ruth, who used to milk our cows, said up to 80 per cent of their business is done through these farmers' markets. The foot and mouth crisis has almost crippled so many local firms.

Duncan artificially inseminated the first three cows of the new season today but Alice found his AI gloves too late. The consequence was not a nice job. Over 50 per cent of the county have not been able to receive an AI service during the crisis, an expensive loss. As a response, an emergency farm gate service has been set up enabling farmers to undertake a simplified technique. The process is similar to that used in the 1967 foot and mouth outbreak when farmers achieved a 50 per cent conception rate. Duncan usually achieves 75 per cent but at least it's a solution until MAFF lifts restrictions.

Calculated our bank balance today and although creditors have been supportive we will need to extend our borrowing. The prospect of having to borrow more fills me with dread and gives me a dull ache in the pit of my stomach. Duncan will not let me write how much extra borrowing we need. Prices have to recover if family farms are to continue. It's not because of a lack of hard work.

Rang the local auctioneers to check out the system of selling stock while markets are closed. The market offices have prepared a list of vendors with stock of all types and ages to sell and a list of potential buyers. We have registered our heifer calves for sale but at what price? We will not be forced to give them away. This system is a temporary solution but nothing like a true market. Imagine selling shares without a stock market. The buyers have no real choice or chance to compare stock while the vendors have no potential in the price or a possibility of a 'good trade'. In most cases the buyer will be aware that the farmer is probably desperate to sell. But as the heifers are costing us £40 per month we need to give the system a chance.

Any sale will require a movement licence, more form filling and a vet's bill to pay for inspecting stock before loading. As markets may not open until the end of the year there are thousands of stock to be traded one way or another.

Friday 27 April. As I sit at the kitchen table a blue-tit is tapping hard on the window, desperate to see off his male challenger. Unbeknown to him it's his reflection. Moss is barking every time he taps, whilst two calves have mooed all morning. Who said the countryside was quiet?

At Membury the pyre was finally lit on Tuesday evening and the sheep carcasses removed. The removal of the stock, albeit twelve days since the outbreak, is such a relief for the family.

I am told that two members of staff are to lose their jobs. We must not forget the knock-on effect of the crisis. The farmer's wife has promised herself a new haircut and serious course of retail therapy when the schedule A restrictions are lifted. I think she deserves them.

The discovery of Phoenix has not only tugged on all our heartstrings but has provided a welcome catalyst in stopping the slaughter of healthy cattle. The other good news is that all the local pubs, restaurants, hotels and B&Bs are full with the world's press, desperate for a picture, and trade is thriving. When she is of legal age the locals owe Phoenix a drink or two.

Saturday 28 April. The number of confirmed cases is thankfully falling but to farmers the threat of the disease is always there. Only yesterday another outbreak was confirmed in Devon in some wonderful pedigree cattle and sheep. Apparently sixteen slaughtermen were on duty and the animals were slaughtered by 6 p.m.

Applied for the licence to move a bull and our young stock. We received a 23 ft fax in reply—the record so far. A movement licence can now be issued by our local vet to reduce MAFF's workload. The target is to produce the licence within two days of application. We shall see.

Enjoyed the school quiz tonight at Sam's school. Even Phoenix made it into a question.

Sunday 29 April. Have just read the views of Nick Brown in the Saturday *Telegraph*. I appreciate that farming practices must change but a Department of Rural Affairs? I would fight against losing the word agriculture. As farmers agriculture is what we do. We must not lose our identity. The style or scale may change but food production is fundamental to agriculture. Food production determines what we put in our mouths.

The Government suggest that the British farmer is to become a 'keeper of the countryside' and not primarily a producer of food. So who is to produce our food? Scale down British agriculture and, if we are not to starve, imports will increase. I know the standards and regulations we are required to keep and we can prove them too. Do we know how Argentine beef or Chinese chickens are reared and slaughtered? Given a choice as a mother I feel it is totally safe to feed my children British food every time. So let's promote it more. Why is British bacon banished to the top three shelves at my local supermarket and not at eye level? Why does cheese from the EU occupy more shelf space than English Cheddar?

I fear we may be swept along with a trend of short-term knee-jerk decisions as a reaction to the foot and mouth crisis. In the process we must not destroy the quality and depth of our home-based agriculture.

Alice and her friend Rozzie plus ponies plus the mobile phone have gone off for a long ride around the lanes whilst Sam is steering the tractor in the wheat fields with Duncan. The opportunity of such simple pleasures reminds me why we still farm—it's not just about making a profit, is it?

PS. But a profit would help.

Monday 30 April. The number of new outbreaks continues to be in single figures, thank goodness.

Four more calves born over the last two days, bringing the total to 71. The problem today was not space but finding barriers. We have used up all our hurdles, gates, old garden fences and even bed heads as calf barriers. I had to resort to the 'we'll never use these old broken hurdles' pile.

Inspired by Heath Robinson plus a bundle of binder twine, I created a shanty-town style calf-pen—and proudly housed four Charolais heifers and asked them to treat my pen with respect. Some hope. Duncan has not give up on the chance of hijacking Misty's stable.

Our total focus is getting the cows back in calf. Cows, like humans, cycle every three weeks with a nine-month gestation. After that the similarities end. We choose the bulls from glossy magazines and the semen arrives frozen in 0.25 cc straws.

Many people have asked me how the process of artificial insemination works. Well, if you are squeamish or eating your breakfast move on to Tuesday instead.

Duncan, who is a trained artificial inseminator, serves the cow by putting his left arm into the cow's rectum and feeling the uterus through the rectal wall. The semen, inserted into a catheter, is then guided through the cervix and into the uterus using his right hand. He then releases the semen and withdraws the catheter. Duncan has 'fathered' hundreds of calves but my suggestion is that you don't shake his left hand.

Once served we record the cow's details. In three weeks we observe her to assess whether she has 'held to service' or has 'returned'. Cows have to be culled if they do not get back in calf but we give them quite a few chances.

May

Tuesday 1 May. A cold and wet afternoon means the cows will have to stay in tonight. Duncan and I spent three hours catching up on paperwork. Crazy, but with so much work to do outside we always feel guilty sitting indoors. However, Duncan always says an hour's planning can earn him just as much as a day's hard work.

Met a friend in town who was concerned over the arrival of a flock of sheep next door to her farm on grass keep-land. Obviously they will have been moved under licence, but having sheep next door to her pedigree Devon cows has unnerved her. The worry of this disease is always with you.

The hawk moth pupa has hatched into an exquisite moth with delicate pink wings. Each year a caterpillar decides to pupate in a pot in the porch for whatever reason. It is very exciting to see the moth emerging. Fed it sugared water before it flew away into the night.

Took Sam to Cubs tonight but completely forgot to collect a friend's son as well. It must be because I've too much to think about as I've never done that before.

Wednesday 2 May. Drove over to Wiveliscombe this morning to deliver some products to a customer. I was aware that I only saw one herd of cows out at grass and two large farms zero-grazing (cutting and carting the grass back into the barns to feed the cows) to minimise the risk of infection. What an expensive operation I thought, is it really worth it?

The one o'clock news confirmed how sensible these farmers were. A foot and mouth outbreak was confirmed in Wiveliscombe, just ten days after the county was given the all-clear. Duncan sprayed the car thoroughly and I washed my clothes. Why did I choose today to drive to Wiveliscombe?

Am staggered to hear on the six o'clock news Anthony Gibson report that possibly the disease was spread as a result of the farmer attending a vaccination course in Hatherleigh. Have MAFF lost all common sense? Why learn how to deal with a fire whilst sitting in the middle of it? Local farmers are incensed and the phone has not stopped ringing.

When shutting up the chickens tonight I noticed the feeder was on its side. A little black bantam hen was trapped inside, alive, but very shocked and with a damaged wing. Settled her in the rabbit hutch to recover.

Thursday 3 May. A second outbreak has been announced in Somerset. The county is in shock as a level of complacency had crept in. To be honest, we have not been as thorough as we should in disinfecting the car and our shoes every time we go out. We felt we had got away with it.

Mr Blair announces the country is on the 'home straight'. Local people feel their crisis is just beginning. The virus will not fit neatly into any election schedules. Too much confidence too soon could be a costly mistake for the Government.

The Somerset farmer involved is a relief milker and travels from farm to farm. The next few days are crucial.

Had a phone call from a friend in Wiveliscombe who is awaiting the valuer and thinks she will lose over 60 'absolutely cracking' Aberdeen Angus cattle. She only turned these cattle out away from the home farm last Friday. The fields are next to a now-confirmed outbreak. The worst part is the waiting. Nobody tells you anything, she said. We feel saddened as some of the cattle were calves we bred and reared. Her home straight is a long way off.

Attempted to wean Treacle, Alice's calf, tonight. She was having none of it and jumped a 4 ft hurdle. As I lost my cool, Alice pointed out this is a sign of a strong, healthy calf. True, but not what I wanted to hear at 9.30 p.m.

Friday 4 May. Having read my diary, the bank manager rang to discuss the increased overdraft we need. With luck, this is just a cash flow problem as the value of 71 calves should cover the extra money, if we can sell them.

Pleased to hear the bank will not charge for this increased facility due to the foot and mouth crisis. The bank manager talked about his farmer clients who followed advice and diversified into tourism. Using the last of their capital to set up holiday cottages or bed and breakfasts, they have now lost, it seems, a whole season's trade.

The good news is that we have found an Aberdeen Angus bull for the heifers, first-time calvers. The cost of moving him from Dorset is £90 to cover the vet inspection and steaming the lorry before and after transportation. The owner has offered to go half and half. We always use an Aberdeen Angus bull as then the heifers calve so easily.

Saturday 5 May. Two more cases reported in the Wiveliscombe area last night. Devastating news. The county veterinary officer rated the seriousness of the outbreak at ten, on a scale of one to ten. The high risk is due to a combination of the farmer having travelled to so many different farms as a relief milker and the area being made up of small units with fields in different parishes.

Spoke to a farmer at the flower market (now Duncan knows I bought some plants). He had driven past a lane blocked off with police tape and notices declaring a foot and mouth outbreak, but only half a mile down the road another sign read 'Footpath now open'. What confused messages.

Mr Blair's message that the 'crisis is over and we can get back to normal' is obviously working in London as two friends thought we were now able to move and sell cattle as before. If only. For 400 farms in Devon still under restrictions until autumn, life is certainly not 'getting back to normal'. For our friends in Cornwall who run Dairyland Farm Park, 150 visitors a day instead of 1,500 shows their crisis is far from over.

It will be six months before farms can restock. I am concerned to read that thousands of dairy cow replacements are ready on the Continent to replace slaughtered stock. Surely any compensation money would be better returned to the UK agricultural economy, and can we be sure of the disease free status of these cows?

The cows are out full-time—such a relief—but it is still cold at night. They galloped up the lane this morning desperate for breakfast.

Sunday 6 May. MAFF vets are testing animals in Exmoor National Park today in the Dulverton area. This is an enormous threat to the magnificent red deer herd and all the tourism that goes with them.

Treacle has calmed down and now drinks from the bucket, much to our relief.

Today there is concern and frustration in the Wiveliscombe area. It seems that MAFF did not know there were any sheep on one of the infected farms until late Saturday. Apparently it has taken two days to convince MAFF, even though the sheep were highly visible to locals. My friend is concerned that this has seriously put at risk more neighbours in the area.

The number of cases is dropping, but the day-to-day problems are increasing for farming and tourism. My real concern is that as statistics improve and foot and mouth becomes old news, farmers' demands for the Government to recognise the continuing crisis will be misinterpreted. It will take time for the countryside to heal its wounds.

MAFF has admitted that possibly only 1 per cent of the 2.5 million animals killed since the epidemic began were actually infected. What a sobering thought.

Monday 7 May. Only four new outbreaks and Somerset, thank God, has been clear for the past four days but the slaughtering at the dangerous contact farms goes on. I think it is fourteen or fifteen farms in total.

After feeding the calves, I drove down to Cornwall for the night with Sam as he has two days off school. The countryside in the May sunshine looked lush and green and belied the underlying tragedy in farming. What a joy to see a field of spring lambs. Once taken for granted, they now produce a special recognition of hope.

Took the decision not to go up to Dairyland as I could bring a risk of infection and, however small, I wouldn't dare put the family and their business at risk.

Duncan meanwhile was filling in the IACS forms at home. Bookwork, not his favourite job, was made more complicated this year. Due to the awful weather and the different drilling dates, many fields are a patchwork of different crops and even areas of failed crops. Consequently, he borrowed a surveyor's wheel and walked the fields recording and plotting out the patchwork. We couldn't predict the effect this would have on one villager. Watching Duncan earnestly pacing and measuring the field next to her house, one villager ran out demanding to know if he was surveying for a new housing development à la *The Archers?* Duncan, now known as the Brian Aldridge of Corfe, rapidly reassured her.

Tuesday 8 May. Well, the election is announced for 7 June. Farming and rural issues should play a central role in the general election debate but I wonder if they will.

The crisis has shown that, although agriculture contributes less than 1 per cent to gross domestic product, it is the basis of a food chain worth billions and the backbone of a rural tourist industry. The past eleven weeks have shown how much we are all affected by farming.

Wednesday 9 May. Cows broke out and chose another field to graze this afternoon. We use an electric fence to keep the cows in but, if they are determined, even that isn't enough. To a cow, different fields produce different flavours and they obviously do not like the one they are in. Spoke to a friend in Devon who is on a form D restriction. Their cows are still not out to grass.

Restricted farms are suffering enormous hardships and many animals are still registered on the welfare scheme. The backlog is enormous: 250,000 animals in Wales and nearly one million in England. One such pig producer in Devon is losing £25 per pig reared since the payments were reduced. Where is the logic in this?

No 116's calf, now the size of a Russian shot-putter, broke out tonight. 'You left the door open', I was told later, after Duncan had rugby-tackled her at the top of the yard. 'Sorry', I murmured from the luxury and depth of a steaming hot bath.

Thursday 10 May. Much relieved to finish the IACS forms and send them off by recorded post.

So the Exmoor farm cattle are to be saved. What a relief for everyone. It seems the farm was no longer classed as a dangerous contact.

Blood tests from a farm linked to this case were negative. I wonder how the other farmers in Somerset feel who were so quickly taken out last week?

Phone call to say the bull is coming tomorrow. It was a late night as Duncan was keen to clean out the shed before the bull arrived. I didn't fancy trying to hold the bull back for the scraper tractor so readily agreed. I'm not very brave with bulls.

Fed the calves late by torchlight accompanied by incredible sheet lightning. Decided to keep the cows in as they would only spend the night sheltering under trees. Last year, after a bad thunderstorm we lost three cows through magnesium deficiency and are desperate for that not to happen again.

As I shut up the chickens, wonderful smell of fresh green apples on the evening air released by the rain splashing on the leaves of the sweet briar hedge. Even Duncan smelt it above the smell of you know what.

Friday 11 May. Five new cases confirmed yesterday, all in the North. I wonder just how much more Cumbria can take. It seems that MAFF press conferences are to be cancelled due to general election procedures. I can't imagine the foot and mouth virus has read the same press release or will adhere to general election rules. Issues such as animal welfare, carcass disposal and culling procedures are very real and immediate to those on the ground. Mr Blair would like it to be 'all quiet on the Western Front' but farmers need reassurance that the Government still cares. We need to be updated on their plans and policies.

The bull arrived bright and early, accompanied by his licence and passport details. By the spring in his step and his nose in the air, it was clear he knew why he had arrived. Introduced him to his fifteen news wives and he immediately said hello.

One neighbouring farmer has come to see our Charolais calves, potentially to buy and rear them on his beef unit. The effects of no market trading for the past three months is enormous as it is the backbone of livestock farming. It's like trying to farm with one arm tied behind your back.

Saturday 12 May. What a glorious day. The world seems a better place when you can feel the warmth of the sun on your back. Cows grazing among buttercups produce an idyllic pastoral scene.

This year we are trying a different method of grazing. Rather than grazing a whole field at once, we are paddock grazing the grass with a back fence behind so that they cannot pick over yesterday's feed. It is more work to move the fences twice a day but the regrowth of grass is incredible.

The cows are milking well but the only problem is their by-product which at this time of year, due to its liquidity, can be projected up to ten feet away.

Milking is a serious case of wearing layers of protective clothing. Thank goodness for the power hose. Strong sunlight is the worst enemy of the foot and mouth virus. So we need a warm, dry month ahead.

The blue-tit is still tapping, albeit at a new window. If he doesn't hurry up and lose his male ego, all the available Miss Blue-tits will have been spoken for.

Sunday 13 May. Today is the last day my diary is to be published in *The Daily Telegraph*. I shall miss writing as I have enjoyed the opportunity but I would have preferred my chance to have come about through different circumstances.

What have I learnt from writing this diary? Primarily, Duncan and I have been overwhelmed by the support, love and prayers of friends and strangers all over the country and world. For example, children in India, vets involved in the 1967 outbreak, a 95-year-old nun and farmers who have lost their animals. For people to have taken the time and trouble to express their feelings is very humbling.

Many urban dwellers have been totally frustrated by how little they can do to help the plight of the farmers and their animals.

They need to know just how much their support does mean to us.

On a lighter note, the bars of chocolate have been a lifeline for late-night calf feeding.

Now the doubts and questions are setting in. I read that 30 per cent of the confirmed cases proved negative in laboratory tests and only 18 per cent of the suspected cases proved positive. The Ministry tries to deny these figures but it is too late as the doubts have set in.

It seems that up to two thirds of those killed might have been killed illegally. What an afterthought for those farmers involved.

But if you were a farmer and you had a form A notice nailed to your front door while an army of white-suited vets marched up your drive, what would you do? You are temporarily disorientated and your emotions are running high. Would you reach for your phone and ring your solicitor or agree to the cull for the good of the nation and your neighbours? What a dreadful dilemma.

After the farms are emptied and disinfected, it is likely a deluge of compensation claims against the Government may be issued. This never happened in 1967 but is surely a sign of our modern times. Will it do any good or should we say it happened, let's learn, restock and move on? Will we lose vital public support our industry needs?

But then how would I feel if it had been our cows? We will all have personal images of this foot and mouth outbreak that will live with us for ever.

I have an image of a farmer's wife, a friend, helping lamb a ewe who had prolapsed only for the ewe to be shot and the lambs injected minutes later. This is not what farming is all about.

Surely the greatest message is what we have learnt through this dreadful crisis? If two and a half million animals have not died in vain we must use these lessons to never ever let such an epidemic sweep through our countryside again.

Though I fear from what I have read that the 2001 report will not look very different to the 1967 report. Yet again it seems that nature is a more powerful force than man.

Single-figure daily outbreaks are greatly encouraging but not front page headline material. Mr Blair has done his best to draw a line under this crisis but in the countryside the knock-on effects will last a long time.

Oh well, 73 calves are calling to be fed. Life goes on. Now where did I hide that chocolate?

Monday 14 May. As foot and mouth continues to cast a black cloud over the countryside, I will carry on recording my personal view of this horrific crisis. I feel it is vitally important that the general public know what is really going on, rather than just have the 'official point of view'.

The Government have announced a £15 million aid package to help rebuild Britain's farming industry. Instead of money the scheme will provide business recovery seminars and a back-up advisory service. I suspect most farmers would have preferred hard cash.

Received an urgent call from the vet asking for the return of the cow lifting net. Another farmer has a cow down. Duncan looked at me and I looked at Duncan. After No 52 had died we thought we had hung it up in the hay shed. We couldn't find it anywhere.

We concluded that when Brian and Duncan cleaned out the shed it went out with the muck. We offered to pay for a new one but the vet just grunted. I do apologise to the farmer waiting and hope he found another net.

Duncan, finally fed up with feeding and bedding up young stock in the sheds, has decided to let them out tonight. Although I usually admire his positive nature, turning out 20 heifers for the first time when it's getting dark into a not very well fenced field was pushing his luck. True to form, the heifers had not read the script and three jumped into the slurry lagoon. The lagoon is deep enough for the heifers to drown, but if they don't struggle the thickness of the slurry might keep them afloat.

Duncan dashed in to ring Geoff to bring his Merlot, a lifting tractor. I murmur concern and support and fight back the desire to say 'I told you so'.

Incredibly the heifers have climbed out of the lagoon and are eating the silage grass in totally the wrong field. As we try to drive them through the right gateway Duncan curses at their stupidity, but to be fair it is now so dark I can hardly see the gateway myself.

There is a lesson to be learnt tonight, but I don't think I'll suggest it until tomorrow.

Thursday 17 May. Happy Birthday Duncan. Milking twice today is probably not the way he would like to spend his birthday. Tea and birthday cake in the parlour break the monotony.

The weeks of relentless culling is taking its toll in the South West. The science behind the contiguous cull is being questioned. Stories of threats and intimidation are being told. The 'Heart of Devon' campaign has just been launched calling for an end to the unnecessary slaughter of healthy animals.

MAFF's policy is to cull all animals contiguous to infected premises up to 56 days after the outbreak. Farmers could appeal, MAFF said, against the cull but only cattle are likely to be reprieved because sheep can 'store' the virus undetected.

Surely it is absurd to slaughter these cattle several weeks after the original outbreak. By then they would have shown clinical signs of the disease and blood tests would confirm a diagnosis. Why not monitor these cattle as an alternative to an immediate cull?

Heard from a farming friend in Devon who has now waited seven weeks for his compensation. Although he has rung them every day for the past three weeks and receives regular promises, nothing has arrived through the post. He obviously has outstanding bills and the additional cost of sowing cereals on land previously grazed by his cows. His has not been a good experience. He was held in a 'time warp' for ten days whilst the Ministry dithered as to whether to cull or not. Finally his cows lay dead around the farm for twelve days before they were removed.

His story is not unique as hundreds of contractors, hauliers and even slaughterers are waiting to be paid. MAFF promised payment 'within fourteen days' but admitted this week they had a backlog. Surely paying extra staff to sort these claims would be a cheaper solution than facing possible future interest claims on delayed payments.

Friday 18 May. Grass continues to grow on infected farms but they have no stock to eat it. Our Devon friends face a dilemma. MAFF are unsure, firstly, as to whether they can ensile forage in disinfected silage pits before the whole farm is approved as 'clean' and, secondly, whether they can sell hay or silage off these fields. Meanwhile the grass continues to grow and our friends await a decision.

Halfway through milking tonight Duncan thought he had put some antibiotic milk in the tank. Milk from cows treated with antibiotics (for mastitis treatment) has to be kept out of the bulk tank away from human consumption for a legal withdrawal period. If any residues are picked up in the tank not only would we be severely financially penalised but should the milk go for processing the residues of antibiotics will affect the cheese-making process. Milk is tested daily as a matter of routine.

We reported the contamination at 8.00 p.m. and a milk inspector arrived at 9.00 p.m. Having tested the milk on the farm he confirmed it was clear. What an efficient service.

Poor No 61 has large warts growing on her teats which makes milking very uncomfortable for her. Consequently she tries to kick Duncan or the cluster off all through milking. Not Duncan's favourite cow.

Saturday 19 May. My father is 80 today. He is a very supportive father and patient grandfather.

To celebrate we had booked into a restaurant on a local farm. A young lad stopped us down the farm drive to spray our car very thoroughly. We were all asked to get out and dip our feet. No problem in wellies, but dainty slingback Italian shoes were more of a challenge. My dear mother, ever keen to do the right thing, went right in and the dip flowed over her toes. No foot and mouth on her tonight.

Busy day helping to run a stall at the Christian Aid plant sale. Sam sold sunflowers for the tallest sunflower competition, in between repeated trips to the cake stall.

Sunday 20 May. MAFF have announced plans to reduce the level of compensation under the welfare disposal scheme. Rates are being dropped to 70 per cent of the 'market value'. The Government declare that they do not want the welfare disposal scheme to be a more attractive option than the market.

Mr Brown, you are missing the point. It is these deserving farmers who do not have the choice. They cannot move their animals to market. The welfare disposal scheme is their only outlet. Just because the Government have been slow to clear the backlog these individual farmers are paying the price. Why should they? Their case is just as deserving as farmers higher up the list.

Some of the baby calves have sore weeping eyes, called 'New Forest Disease', spread by a particular fly. Left untreated a white opaque layer grows over the lens and causes permanent blindness. Treated early it can be cured.

But first catch your calf. These calves are loose and running around a shed 45 feet by 30. I'm so glad I opted for the management role, simply suggesting which calf to catch next. It is an advantage to be a woman sometimes.

Tuesday 22 May. Cuckoo, cuckoo rang out through the valley.

Hearing the cuckoo for the first time never fails to excite me and was top news on the tennis court this morning.

Shocked to see a fox standing in the middle of the chicken paddock in the afternoon sunshine, whilst the hens had flattened themselves against the wire fence, hoping not the be seen. What a brash fox. Probably they are feeding cubs. Moss saw him off but he'll be back.

Farm leaders in Yorkshire said MAFF had withheld essential information about the number of infected farms and contiguous cases around the Settle area. It is thought that 100,000 animals will have to be slaughtered.

Animals are being transported off farms in Yorkshire for disposal in Cumbria and Cheshire. Many locals feel the Government are determined to avoid images of burning pyres so near the election. No good for votes, you know.

Thursday 24 May. The lack of information for farmers is producing an air of suspicion and mistrust on farms. By scrapping their regular press conferences, the Government have created an information vacuum.

The true cost of this crisis is staggering. The Ash Moor burial site in North Devon has cost taxpayers (you and me) £7.5 million. If the pit is eventually used to house carcasses from infected areas it will cost another £5 million in maintenance costs. This pit was built too slowly, too late, whilst the carcasses lay stinking in piles around Devon farmyards.

Sadly, a ten-day-old calf died this evening. It is our fault as the calf never had enough colostrum (mother's first milk—full of antibodies) and was consequently vulnerable to any bug. Colostrum must be given within 8–12 hours of birth before a special opening—the oesophageal groove—closes, shutting off direct access to the calf's stomach.

Usually we milk the cow at birth and feed this first milk from a bottle to the calf to ensure its protection. In this case we must have been too busy. What a costly mistake.

Friday 25 May. Watched the news today to see the sheep being rounded up for culling on the Yorkshire Dales. It broke my heart to see the pictures of these proud mothers unwittingly leading their lambs to slaughter. Lambs are a symbol of new life, not death and destruction. I can only imagine the distressing noise as the ewes were taken from their lambs.

With only two weeks to go before the election the Government are choosing to keep details of the outbreak in the so-called 'Settle Rectangle' to a minimum.

Farmers are being asked to sign the Data Protection Act (or is it the Official Secrets Act?) before they can clean and disinfect their farms. I thought this was used in the interests of national security, not to enable a government department to cover up its blunders.

Headline tonight announces a possible risk of dioxin emissions from pyres and warns consumers of the dangers of milk products produced from a farm within that area. The danger area is land within a mile of the pyres, which means a very, very low risk, but to the public the headline shouts 'Milk carries cancer risk'.

Too little information can be dangerous and if in doubt the consumer will not buy the product. After such a headline, it requires months of reassurance and promotion to recover those lost sales.

If only the true facts were published. I quote from a paper sent to farmers from the Food Standards Agency:

> We have concluded that, based on the information we have so far, there is unlikely to be any increased public health risk for the vast majority of people who consume milk or dairy products produced on land within two kilometres of the pyres. But there may be a slightly higher, although still very small, risk for farmers and their customers who consume milk and milk products exclusively from such a source in the coming weeks.

The public will have no idea from which farm their four pints of supermarket milk originate but the seed of doubt has been sown.

Saturday 26 May. Britain has only just banned all beef imports from Brazil, Argentina, Uruguay and Paraguay, following continued outbreaks of foot and mouth in those countries. Previously, beef was only banned from infected regions in Brazil. But in the past two weeks Brazil has seen five new outbreaks. Knowing how the virus in this country has no respect for boundaries, why was meat still being imported from parts of Brazil?

Am suddenly aware that my middle finger feels stiff and sore and has swollen quite badly. Earlier today I tried to inject a calf, missed and injected myself instead. I suspect I've an infection developing in the finger. Can't worry now as too many calves to feed. Must be bad as I can't carry any buckets in my right hand and Alice has to turn off the TV and help me.

Duncan finished milking and rushed back to the Cub Camp, staying until Monday morning. He loves everything about camping, probably because there is not a cow in sight, but Sam misses his home comforts.

Sunday 27 May. Local sheep are desperate to be sheared. Sheep shearing produces a significant risk of transmitting foot and mouth, but for animal welfare reasons it must be allowed to go ahead. The greatest risk is if shearers are allowed to move freely from infected to controlled areas. MAFF therefore have set up a licence system.

In an infected area farmers can only use a shearer who possesses a red licence (infected area licence). Outside these areas any sharers with a green licence can be used. Shearers have to carry proof of identity and a log-book recording visits to previous farms and disinfecting procedures.

What a lot of paperwork and red tape, but absolutely crucial to limit the spread of this disease, especially as sheep are involved.

Small emergency at lunchtime as Alice, having set off to ride around the lanes, rang most concerned that Misty was distressed and shaking. The mobile phone is a lifeline when she rides off on her own. When I arrived, Misty had calmed a little but was showing genuine symptoms of fear. It seems she would not go past a van parked in the road, belonging to the local butcher. Did the smell of blood and meat frighten her? Animals have a very sensitive nose for smells.

Misty's fear reminded me of an incident that happened a few years ago when I was taking the cows down the lane after morning milking.

The lane has steep banks on either side zigzagged by animal runs, regular routes they use to cross the lane. What looked like a wild mink crossed only a few feet in front of me and ran up the opposite bank. I was well ahead of the cows and I doubt if any of them saw it.

However, as the lead cows came up to where the mink had crossed, they all stopped, snorted, breathed heavily, stamped their feet and would not cross over the imaginary line. They showed real fear and tried to turn back. But the cows at the back, unaware of the situation, kept on walking and jamming up the front cows.

All hell let loose, just like a commuter trying to go in the opposite direction on Waterloo station in the rush hour. Soon the whole herd picked up on the panic and they all tried to turn around.

Eventually, we managed to drive them down the lane but they were genuinely frightened.

Considering cows are such phlegmatic creatures, had I not seen the mink cross I would never have understood what brought about such a change in character. But why does a mink frighten a cow?

June

Saturday 2 June. Local footpaths officially open today. The area to the west of Taunton is still closed due to the Wiveliscombe outbreak. We have applied for exemption of the footpaths that pass through the grass fields, believing there still to be a risk from walkers and dogs. The new signs are a not very subtle shade of purple—designed to be an 'apolitical' colour. They threaten a fine of £5,000.

I learnt a lesson today. Never rush a decision. Whilst we were away for the night I sold four fantastic calves over the phone without thinking the deal through. The result is that I've sold them far too cheaply. Duncan, a man of his word, would never renege on a deal. I know what's done is done, but each time I feed them it reminds me of my mistake.

Setting prices without a market is proving hard. As I read today, 'the vital importance of the prices produced in open public competition at auction cannot be over-emphasised'. How true.

The second lesson I have learnt is that although a price is set it may take ten to fourteen days to secure a licence and transport for the calves. Meanwhile, the animals still need feeding—who carries that cost? We do. At market the deal is done and the animal sold on the same day.

Sunday 3 June. Have been trying really hard to hear or read of any news of rural policies from any of the three main political parties. How do they plan to support and rebuild the countryside? How do they plan to improve the confidence of the consumer in British agriculture?

Have I missed very much? I suspect not. For the community in the Settle area of the Yorkshire Dales the election must be a total non-event. But they have not even had one syllable of recognition from any minister.

The past week's election campaign appears to have been

dominated by taxation policy. The last thing that affects us is a penny on income tax. Like most farmers we haven't produced a taxable profit for the past two years and don't expect to in the near future.

Total nightmare in sorting out the calf passports. Have just spent over an hour on the phone chasing the last batch of 27 passports I sent in last week. They cannot be found in the system at all. Keep calm.

Wednesday 6 June. Enough is enough. Mr Fox has pushed his luck. Once again he called in for his lunchtime snack at around 1.30—usually just before *The Archers*. Alerted by chickens squawking, we rushed outside and nearly fell over the fox. He was by the back door with a red hen in his mouth. Two shouting humans and a barking dog were too much for him and he dropped the hen. Amazingly, she simply shook herself, sorted out her ruffled feathers and walked off. That's one 'cool chicken', as the children would say.

Have just spent two hours on the phone sorting out calf passports. It is such a waste of time but it must be done. The British Cattle Movement Service are very helpful, but they require so much information and detail. I do wonder if other members of the EU have such an accurate livestock recording system as in the UK. I very much doubt it.

Tea-time squawking. Having missed lunch, the fox returned for tea. Duncan, seeing a flash of red in the chicken paddock, crept around the garden with his gun. With an expert shot the fox was killed outright. On close inspection he was an old dog fox.

The children were interested to see a fox so close and seemed to cope with a dead animal very well. Farm life exposes the children to 'life and death' on every level, a great way to learn life's lessons.

Thursday 7 June. 'Goggle-Eyes', a three-day-old Charolais bull calf, is not well. As a result of a difficult calving his eyes are bloodshot and very prominent. He is scouring and becoming dehydrated. We treat him homeopathically with pyrogene and aconite.

Voted at the local village hall and tried to answer all Alice's questions about the voting system. The footpath by the village hall is now open. The field is growing an excellent crop of winter wheat and it seems such a shame to strike a track right across the middle of the field. To re-route footpaths around the edge of the field where less damage would be done can be done but incurs a high cost.

Rang one of our calf buyers for details of the licence to hear the shocking news of an outbreak at North Newton, a village four miles north of Taunton. Shattering news. A shiver runs through me and serves to remind me just what a threat foot and mouth still is. So many people have closed the book on this crisis but it still has many chapters to run.

By coincidence, Duncan met Derek in town tonight. As he had just valued the suspected herd he cannot go back to his wife and family on the home farm. He booked into a local hotel. He is considered 'clean' after three days.

Friday 8 June. Nearly overslept this morning as, in a fit of madness, I stayed up late to watch the election results. Had to offer to do the pony and chickens on Alice's behalf as it was my fault we were late.

How interesting that the foot and mouth crisis produced its own 'Peter Snow computer image', demonstrating how the outbreak has affected voting in the worst areas. The results showed a 3 per cent drop in Labour and a 2.6 per cent increase for the Conservatives. This suggests to me a rural vote against the Government's handling of the foot and mouth crisis.

Finally managed to fax through the three long-distance movement licences. It seems I had been using the wrong fax number, which explains why the line was busy even at 2.00 a.m.

Have just been asked to fax licences through again. It amazes me how a fax can get lost in mid-air. Incredibly, I have calculated that I have spent over eleven hours sorting out details and passports just to move 44 calves. In pre-foot and mouth days the calves would simply be loaded up for Taunton market.

Usually I would go in and see them sold. This has two advantages. Firstly, I think the auctioneer tries a little harder if he sees you at the ringside. Secondly, I reward myself with a quite yummy warm pork and apple sauce roll and a cup of coffee. I miss those rolls.

Saturday 9 June. Well, the election results are through. In our constituency the Lib-Dem majority was overturned and the Conservative candidate won by 200 votes after two re-counts. I suspect the rural vote went against the Lib-Dem candidate (who is anti-hunting) as the area covers part of Exmoor.

The North Newton outbreak has been confirmed, much to the shock of the whole area. Large red road signs declaring 'foot and mouth infected area' have been set up on the roads leading into Taunton. The effect of seeing the signs so close to home is very threatening. To the majority of drivers it probably means very little, but to us the signs evoke such emotion.

Rang the vet at Culmhead to confirm the limit of the infected area. The line has been drawn along the road at the end of Heale Lane, only half a mile away. We are that close. Had we been within the area all stock movements would be cancelled and no calf sales. Not sure I could cope with a summer of 85 calves.

Neighbours rang to say the road by the local pub was closed, with the police directing traffic away. This is worrying, as it suggests a possible new outbreak. A call to local farmers and auctioneers reveals nothing. Duncan calls the police who report the computers have gone down, but they will follow up the call. A friend and I decide to drive out and investigate for ourselves. We solve the mystery. The sign reads 'Village Fete today at 2.00 p.m.'. Cars queuing by the pub for the car park, marshalled by luminous yellow-jacketed attendants, had produced a foot and mouth rumour. At least we are safe.

Sunday 10 June. Awoke to sunshine again. The view from our bed is glorious, through the Heale Valley and on towards Corfe Hill. The grass fields rise gently towards the woods, a tapestry of different shades of green. Bill's seventeenth-century cottage nestles under the wood. I know how privileged we are to enjoy such a view and I try not to take it for granted. Duncan just wishes he had more time in bed to enjoy the view.

On a still night you can hear the cows tearing at the grass. Cows only have a bottom set of teeth and hence use their tongues to tear at the grass. Sheep, however, having a full set, can bite the grass with their teeth. This is why sheep can graze a pasture down so tight.

Sarah, a solicitor friend, gave some of her precious time to go through the publisher's contract. It's all new to me but I did suggest I could help her with the fertiliser policy on her lawn. Not much of a trade.

Cooked a proper Sunday lunch, as I felt I had been neglecting the family, of delicious Devon lamb collected from a local farm. You can taste the difference.

Good news. Little 'Goggle-Eyes' has drunk from a bucket on his own for the first time. Sam takes him for a walk around the garden each day.

Monday 11 June. Three new cases announced on the North Yorkshire Moors. Who said this crisis was over? This has thrown the tourist industry into despair as the footpaths had only just been opened. Could this be how the disease is spreading?

Waited anxiously for the postman to arrive. For my movement jigsaw puzzle to work, the 27 calf passports would have to arrive today. I'm like a little girl at Christmas, waiting for the post.

Thank goodness I'm saved. All the passports have arrived safely.

After the Charolais bull arrives tomorrow we will be under a 21-day ban and not allowed to move any livestock off the premises. Duncan announces that he is desperate to move the heifers on to the hill as they keep breaking out. This means I have to arrange a local movement licence within twelve hours. No problem, he says. He tests my patience.

A miracle. Thank you, MAFF. The licence was approved in only four hours. A record.

Am desperate to sell 'Survivor', the 16-month-old Belgian Blue runt. His broad head and big horns are totally out of proportion to his short little legs. He walks through or under any fence and simply roams around the farm. Desperate to sell, we have even resorted to 'buy one, get one free' but even that hasn't worked. Any offers welcomed.

Duncan spoke to the vet who first diagnosed the outbreak at North Newton. The suspected animal lay in the corner of the shed away from the others, the skin from his tongue virtually fallen away. It was without doubt a case of foot and mouth.

MAFF vets visited our neighbours today. Because their shearer had been working in the infected area last week they have been issued with a form D. Stock will be checked every two days. They were due to sell a group of fat lambs and four freshly calved heifers today, but the licence arrived too late. As they are beef and sheep farmers, milking the freshly calved heifers is a real problem. They are ringing around for a portable milking machine.

Problems such as these demonstrate the long-term effect of foot and mouth. Even though, statistically, the outbreak is 'under control' rural problems are still very real.

Tuesday 12 June. 'D Day' or C for Calf Day today. Quick diversion into the agricultural merchants to repair the knapsack sprayer. So vital to be extra vigilant today, so we must spray every vehicle thoroughly.

Two of the buyers are coming from an infected area on to our farm, a clean area. The ruling is that no animals can come out of an infected area, but stock may be brought in. How do we calculate the risk factor of their visit? Should any of these farms become a suspicious outbreak, we immediately would become a dangerous contact farm. What new terminology we have all learnt. It seems second nature now to use these terms.

The day was supposed to run like clockwork, but in the afternoon we had a major problem.

But first, the vet was booked for a morning visit. His official duty was to examine every animal being sold, check the ear tags and, if completely satisfied, issue the licences. As we had applied for four licences the paperwork took longer than the inspection.

It was my lucky day as Nick was the duty vet. He is young and handsome and quite cheered me up. He had been called into Devon a few weeks ago, when he identified clinical cases of foot and mouth. When cattle display signs of the virus there is no doubt of diagnosis. He described, when checking cow's tongues, the whole layer of skin come off in his hand.

It is in sheep that the disease is difficult to diagnose and on some farms cattle have been penned with sheep to indicate early warning signs. Rather like the case of the canary bird used down the mines.

All was approved and we waited for the first lorry to arrive.

This local distance movement licence did not require the lorry to be sealed at the point of destination, for the cattle were under our control. It is land we rent on the hill.

The success rate of loading a bull and 15 heifers on to a lorry can go either way. Duncan, the eternal optimist, always says 'They'll be OK', whereas I always like to be doubly sure and set up extra gates. Between us we find a way. As long as one animal walks up the ramp, the others will follow, but if not the front row turn around and force their way back through a 'one-way street'. Lots of shouting and occasional 'after the watershed' words and they were loaded.

Meanwhile the ADAS supervisor had arrived to check all lorries arriving and leaving. I knew John from the days I worked in the Milk Marketing Board so it was good to see a friendly face.

The second lorry arrived. Two very strong four-month-old Charolais bulls had to be rounded up from the suckler yard. Their last contact with a human was when Duncan pulled them out into this world, but they weren't about to return any favours. Duncan's rodeo skills were put to the test. I scored him one for style, but ten out of ten for determination.

When the third lorry arrived Duncan, desperate to get on, went to open the tailgate totally unaware of the significance of the official seal. The supervisor crossed the yard in one giant leap shouting 'Stop, stop', terrified Duncan had messed up the system. Loaded the four quality bull calves I had undersold. At least they can't remind me of my mistake any more.

And then we waited for the lorry collecting the big batch of 30 calves. And we waited. Believing there to be a queue at the disinfecting centre at the market, we weren't too worried. The bull was due to arrive at 4.30—our deadline. After that no stock could leave the farm for 21 days and we were desperate to sell these calves.

After an hour and a half I went in to find the number of the haulier. The details had been arranged by the auctioneers. I'll never forget that sinking feeling when the driver, in a reply to 'Where are you?', said 'Don't know nothing about it dear'. Panic. No way could he be cleaned, sealed and here within the half hour of the bull arriving.

I feared the deal was off until MAFF agreed that, if we could keep the bull away from the calves until they went next morning, the licence was still valid. We unloaded Mr Bull on to the hill fields, with two willing volunteer bovine companions, and breathed a sigh of relief.

Interested to learn from the lorry driver that there has been a total ban of any animals going into Dorset (the bull's home) since the first outbreak in mid February. Dorset has had no cases of foot and mouth.

Finished off the evening with friends Margi and Andrea at the local Chinese. It was good to talk and unwind and not mention foot and mouth.

Wednesday 13 June. Duncan up extra early to get the work done before the lorry arrived to pick up the calves. As I am off on the village garden club outing today, I have sprayed all the heifers to go with a red dot on their heads. As the 30 calves are divided between eight different sheds, loading should be fun. I shall think of them all when relaxing over a cup of coffee.

The Somerset countryside was looking wonderful. The drive up to the house was a perfect English rural scene. We looked across fields of buttercups, where sheep grazed and lambs bleated under the shade of broad spreading oak trees, to see Wells Cathedral standing proudly in the Vale of Avalon.

I came back to empty calf-pens and a new peace in the main calf-shed. Bliss. Sam's little calf, 'Goggle Eyes', is all alone but comes out for walks two or three times a day. Our goal is to get him better so he can join his friends in the suckler cow group. Sam now tells me that 'Goggle Eyes' is a horrible name and very cruel. He is now called 'Prince'.

Yesterday, after we sold the group of big suckled calves, we moved in six new baby calves to take their place. Calves always do better the natural way than bucket fed. What must the surrogate mums have thought when they found their calves had shrunk overnight? They seemed totally unfazed and carried on as though nothing had changed. Such is their love of calves.

It seems that after the local outbreaks the parish council has taken the decision to shut the footpaths again, ten days after they were opened. I feel sorry for the local dogs as they won't know if they are coming or going.

Came in late to listen to a disturbing message on the answerphone. My friend near Wiveliscombe reported she had just found a cow with symptoms of a heavy cold, streaming from its nose and mouth. I went cold when I heard the news. Too late to ring her now.

Thursday 14 June. 'Whatever happened to foot and mouth?' was the headline on GMTV this morning when I watched Noel Edmonds's passionate plea for the countryside. The past tense of that headline suggests the public and media's view of this crisis.

Past tense? Try telling that to the people of Settle, who received virtually no support or recognition from government ministers during the elections. Try telling that to the thousands of farms still in restricted areas.

Disgusted to read that the word Agriculture is not even included in the title of the all-embracing new ministry, the Department for Environment, Food and Rural Affairs, or DEFRA for short. Said quickly, which none of the ex-MAFF telephonists can yet do, it sounds like 'Death Row'. Is there a hidden agenda?

What a direct snub to farming folk. The Government have done their best to destroy farming and now agriculture is not even recognised in the corridors of Whitehall. Politicians may argue that it's really all about food, but food is what consumers buy. Agriculture is how you produce it.

Arguably, other member states have combined ministries of agriculture with rural affairs, but Britain is the only EU country to erase the name of the industry. I only hope Mrs Beckett is a quick learner.

Friday 15 June. Another outbreak is confirmed in Somerset. The total is now six in a very small cluster on the Devon-Somerset border. Jo, the Aberdeen Angus breeder, rang this morning. She is resigned to losing a group of cattle that have grazed in an adjacent field to an outbreak, but is frustrated as she had no contact from the Ministry at all. Emotions are running very high in that area and she rang the newsdesk on the *Daily Mail* to update them on the situation. She was amazed at their reaction. Once they established that she was a farmer, they became quite hostile, cut her short and declared that 'The story wasn't for them'. Would this suggest the media is under some kind of pressure from above?

Cow 108 is lame, but something else is wrong. She is very listless and is neither eating nor cudding. This is the first cow I have been seriously worried about and know I must check her feet and mouth. From what I can tell, there are no obvious symptoms. Unbeknown to me, Duncan had had the same worries and had also checked the cow. All we can do is keep a careful eye on her.

So fed up with a blocked drain that I had to clear it. There is something very satisfying in clearing drains, when the water bubbles and suddenly goes whoosh. Cleared, success.

It was after 10.00 p.m. when I finally finished and yet it was only just getting dark. Too tired to cope with squabbling children or to face the washing up, so I sat outside for a while. The bats were flying overhead and I could count at least six. Tried to see whether they were roosting (is that the right word?) in the barn or under the eaves of the house. The garden smells sweetest and purest at night, so it was with great reluctance that I finally went in. Ignored the washing up and walked on by up to bed.

Saturday 16 June. Having seen the list of local outbreaks, many dear friends have been ringing to check if we are OK. Their continued support means so much to us.

My decision to clear the drain late last night has created a problem this morning. The cleared drain cover is now visible to the cows who imagine it to be a 100-ft deep ravine or something worse. They will not cross it. We started off understanding their concern and gently coaxing them to cross. After five minutes the tone in our voices changed and they were not 'ladies' any more. Finally, I had to lay straw over the drain cover. The little black heifer stepped back, took a run and took off two paces too early and dropped a back leg—four faults but at least she was over.

We knew we must check 108 again and coaxed her into the crush for a closer inspection. Her mouth was still clear, but there was a nasty infection in her front foot. This is probably why she has been feeling so rough. Sam, who helped us, injected her under Duncan's supervision. After my experience last week I'm keeping well away from needles.

Another late night. This is crazy, as Duncan is regularly working from 7 in the morning until 10.30 or 11 every night. He is exhausted. It is a vicious circle. The later he goes to bed the later he gets up in the morning, until he is almost becoming nocturnal. Tomorrow is Father's Day. He deserves to be spoilt.

Sunday 17 June. Duncan has his first lie-in for weeks. Woke him with a cup of tea, Father's Day cards and a supply of Yorkie bars. We almost feel guilty eating chocolate in bed at 9.30 a.m. with the Sunday papers, but it's wonderful. Suddenly, disturbed shouts of 'You bastards' from Mike. The cows have gone up instead of down the lane. That'll teach us for lying in bed.

Monday 18 June. Another outbreak is announced outside Wellington. Rumours are flying high about the source of infection in the area. The Ministry vets are working on the theory that the virus may have been lying dormant in one of the sheep flocks in the area for some time. The virus was then reactivated by stress, possibly induced by shearing.

Another theory put forward by a vet working in the 1967 crisis is that 'dirty' vets could be spreading the disease. They are judged 'clean' after only three days of dealing with an infected farm.

However, a period of three weeks was recommended after the last epidemic.

These are fundamental questions that must be answered if this disease is not to drag on until the end of the year.

Officials are only human and mistakes do happen. A farmer friend told me how a vet, having examined her outlying stock grazing adjacent to a confirmed case, asked to inspect her cows at Home Farm. 'No way', she exclaimed. That would establish a dangerous contact and put her cows at risk. She asked for a so-called 'clean' vet.

Why is it that when we have a deadline, such as finishing this book, we are easily distracted. Today, instead of writing, I have made a gooseberry fool, elderflower cordial and baked a Victoria sponge. At least Duncan is pleased to have something to eat.

We are planning to make silage at the end of this week. The forecast suggests the week will be fine and warm. Silage is principally ensiled grass producing an anaerobic respiration. If grass and oxygen combine and aerobic respiration occurs compost is produced, so it is crucial to keep the air out of the silage. Silage is either made into big bales (the black puddings seen in fields) or in a large pile called a silage clamp. It is vital to keep the clamp clean of muck or soil or else the silage is contaminated.

Every night when I feed 'Goggle Eyes' he comes out for an evening walk. He is quite in a routine and shuts the chickens up with me each night.

Tuesday 19 June. Each day we check the heifers and bull on the hill. Lovely setting and great views, but adjacent to the golf-course with its well-cut fairways and manicured greens, only a hedge away from our stock.

No worries, until their grass becomes coarse and stemmy in midsummer and they begin to wander. Our nightmare is to receive a phone call—'Do you own some black and white cows and a bull?'. I dread to think of the damage they could do overnight before being discovered in the morning.

Last year, after one such outbreak, I spent a busy afternoon delivering four bottles of wine as a thank-you to people who had helped on the round-up. Sometimes sorry is not enough. Such as last September when a single heifer jumped into a garden and danced the afternoon away on his newly seeded lawn. She even had the cheek to be sitting in the middle of the lawn when the owners returned. That deserved more than a bottle of wine.

Spoke to Andrea, the wife of the local valuer, tonight. She has run the farm on her own for the past week as her husband is considered 'too dirty' to come home. Different people are paying a different price due to this dreadful virus.

Friday 22 June. Mrs Beckett has made her first mistake. She has refused to order a full public inquiry into the foot and mouth crisis. Surely the scale of the epidemic justifies such an inquiry. If we are to protect ourselves against the horrors of another outbreak questions must be answered and lessons learnt. It is fundamental to establish how the disease reached this country.

Many tears have been shed in the Clayhanger area this week. Lives have been deeply scarred. A nine-year-old farmer's son proudly took the valuer around his father's pedigree cattle but finally broke down when he saw eight slaughtermen, carrying the tools of their trade, entering the farm gate.

Farming children have witnessed some terrible sights during the crisis. I know of one little girl aged ten whose job was to spray the pile of dead sheep with disinfectant every day in an attempt to disguise the smell of rotting carcasses. She simply accepted it as her job to do.

Duncan is busy topping the pastures. Topping produces a very high cut to remove weeds and seed heads to encourage fresh regrowth. The ground is very dry and we are desperate for rain.

The last two calves have been born and are still in the fields. Every time Mum comes in for milking they find a place to hide until she returns. Poor Alice, who was moving Misty's fence yesterday unaware of these calves, was startled when one little Charolais calf jumped out of the nettles right in front of her. I heard her scream from the kitchen. These calves are becoming wild. However will we ear-tag them?

Alice is fed up with Dad and the cows. Every day the cows

walk through into Misty's paddock knocking down the fencing. Each morning before school she has to put up the fence again before she can turn Misty out. Dad pinched the fencer for the cows so the fence is not electrified. Alice was furious. Two months ago he pinched the paddock gate as well. Ponies are not Duncan's priority.

Saturday 23 June. Busy day. Duncan and Sam are camping at Cub Camp whilst I'm running the plant stall at the school fete. For the sake of Duncan's sanity it is vital he gets away from the farm for the day.

No 108 is still very lame, as the stones had penetrated very deeply. The wound will take a long time to heal. We are injecting her daily to keep the infection under control. Cows are so reliant on having four good feet. Left her in the orchard with water and hay rather than walk her up and down the lane.

Modern methods of road surfacing when tiny stones are laid on wet tar cause enormous problems for the cows. As they wear loose it is these little stones that can do so much harm.

The local auctioneer has just finished twelve consecutive days valuing, sometimes four farms a day. He described what a lonely job it is returning to a sterile hotel room each night, as memories of the day stay around to haunt him.

Sunday 24 June. Another warm and sunny day. Finished an article for *The Daily Telegraph* by the copy time of 3 p.m. Nothing like a deadline to make you write. Helped by listening to the omnibus edition of *The Archers* and a breakfast of chocolate croissants.

Glad to have the opportunity to keep the profile of foot and mouth in the news. This disease needs a human face and human stories or else the Government's plans to put foot and mouth in the past tense will have been successful.

Monday 25 June. Outbreaks today confirmed in the Brecon Beacons area of South Wales. This is a new hot spot and over 10,000 animals are due to be slaughtered. Who can predict where the next hot spot will erupt? There is a continual anxiety that it could be us next.

Flies, flies, flies. Hot weather, an Aga and a farmyard are the combination for a serious fly infestation in the kitchen. I hate them. Everything has to be covered or put away. The children delight in reciting their newly discovered knowledge of how a fly digests its food. Don't ask.

Am distressed to read a mailshot from the Soil Association. The front cover is an aerial photograph of a herd of cows being destroyed due to the foot and mouth crisis. Live cows are standing next to the cows already shot whilst two ghostly white-suited slaughtermen walk amongst the herd completing their task. The title of the picture reads 'There is no such thing as cheap food'.

I take issue with their arguments. First, they suggest that modern farming methods set up to produce cheap food have made us vulnerable to foot and mouth. There is no evidence whatever to support this theory. Why not use a photograph of meat imported from countries where foot and mouth is endemic to represent the effects of cheap food. Or a photograph of a dead monkey smuggled in a suitcase into Heathrow, a likely cause of entry of the virus in this country.

And second, it suggests organic farming methods would not have encouraged foot and mouth. Why is it then that when the virus was jumping from farm to farm in the Hatherleigh area of Devon, it did not recognise an organic farm from a non-organic farm but struck regardless.

I am saddened the Soil Association has used such manipulative emotion and confusing facts to mislead the public. I am so incensed I shall be writing to them. Watch this space.

The forecast suggests thunderstorms and rain across the whole area tomorrow afternoon. Duncan is in a dilemma as to whether to cut the grass for silage. Ideally, silage should be cut in the sun to produce higher sugar levels in the grass, and ensiled before too much energy is lost to respiration. We decide to wait and watch the forecast tomorrow morning.

Tuesday 26 June. The Government had promised to match donations to the Foot and Mouth Fighting Fund pound for pound.

In March, Environment Minister Michael Meacher said he 'strongly supported' the 'Green Wellie' appeal and would be delighted to match it pound for pound.

Why am I not surprised to learn today that they are backtracking? It seems they will match private donations but not those made by 'corporate' donors. Even Church donations are being classified as corporate. But from where did those donations originate? From the local parishioners, of course.

Read a letter today from a lady who had received a very welcome contribution from the Addington Fund. It seems that if the monies are used for personal benefit, such as the supermarket bill, the income will not be taxed. However, if the monies are used for trading purposes such as buying cattle feed, the income will be taxed. What a cheek. The money was of course donated by the public from taxed income.

The fact that foot and mouth disease and the resulting countryside crisis were not even mentioned in the Queen's Speech is an insult to farmers and a strong belief that single-figure outbreaks give the Government the right to close the chapter on foot and mouth. The only reference to rural issues is the promise to give time for yet another vote on hunting. This is a frightening indication of Labour's priorities for its second term.

Wednesday 27 June. Mr Blair will still not commit himself to a public inquiry. With losses to tourism of £5 billion and farmers losing £25 million per month, questions must be answered. Since the election all the ministers, except the Prime Minister, responsible for foot and mouth have been removed and as a result are no longer accountable for their previous actions.

Taxpayers are picking up the bill. They deserve the courtesy of an itemised bill.

Shared a cup of tea with a lovely gentleman, a retired vet, who was practising 50 or 60 years ago. What a different picture he painted of previous foot and mouth outbreaks. He was called out one Sunday in the 1940s to find a lonely cow tethered to a post in a field. Immediately he was suspicious by the way she was moving her weight from one leg to another, as though marching on the spot. She was dribbling and on inspection the complete top layer of the tongue came off in his hand. A Ministry vet had to be called from Yeovil and the diagnosis confirmed. The whole herd was destroyed that night and a fire lit. This was an isolated outbreak and no spread occurred. Neighbouring farms were checked every day rather than culled outright. The key was that the time from diagnosis to disposal was under 24 hours. I believe the spread of the outbreak during this crisis was the fundamental error in the time it took from diagnosis to slaughter, let alone disposal. Will we never learn? The speed at which this outbreak spread also suggests to me that the virus was around before February, laying a foundation of destruction.

Duncan has been helping our neighbours bring in their silage. I can see his pleasure in driving around in a very smart tractor with a stereo radio. Just for once, if a machine breaks down, it is not his problem.

Three hens are broody and desperate for chicks. Having lost our lovely Light Sussex hens to the fox, I am searching for some fertile eggs. Light Sussex hens are the hens of the nineteenth-century farmyards, producing wonderful eggs.

'Sitting on eggs' is a clever affair. A clutch of eggs can vary in age between one and twelve days, the hen having laid only one egg a day. When the hen finally sits to incubate the eggs they will eventually hatch on the same day whatever the original age of the egg. This is why I can bring in a clutch of cold eggs, but know the hen will 'kick start' the whole process into action. Each day she turns the eggs, maintaining a constant temperature whatever the weather. Isn't nature marvellous.

Thursday 28 June. We would like to have cut the grass today but the contractor's mower is still broken. Each day the grass matures, becoming coarse and stemmy. This lowers the 'D' value (energy value) of the grass, producing silage of a lower feed value.

Friday 29 June. No 30, a suckler cow, has mooed all night only 20 feet from our bedroom window, as we have taken her away from the calves. This is taking motherhood a little too far. If only she would vary the tune. Duncan, exhausted from another late night, shut all the bedroom windows. I didn't dare say I was too hot.

The Government are still being criticised for not making a decision on the inquiry business. Face your responsibilities, Mr Blair, and order a public inquiry. The Government were quick enough to scrutinise the handling of the BSE crisis by the Conservatives. As I understand it, Mr Blair himself would be questioned at a public inquiry. Does this possibility cause him any concern?

The contractors are mowing the silage grass. Duncan and I walked the fields anxious to assess the yield. Serious problem of rabbits in the hill fields. The field has been eaten down as tight as a bowling green along the edge of one side of the field, 30 feet out from the hedge.

It is worth considering that one cow is equivalent to five sheep, and five rabbits are equivalent to one sheep. With an average litter size of five, and a potential six litters per doe per season, we have a lot of uninvited 'cow equivalents' eating our grass.

Alice is baby-sitting two pet rats for a school friend. However hard I try I cannot disassociate these rats from their brown disease-bearing farmyard relatives. I think it is the tail that does it for me. We are all on full alert to keep Moss the dog away, a champion rat killer.

Saturday 30 June. Confirmed cases now top 1,800. Add this to the estimate from DEFRA of 1,450 extra cases within the dangerous contact cull to bring the total to over 3,200. This compares to 2,364 outbreaks in 1967. Thank God the West Country has been clear now for twelve days.

Intensive blood testing is taking place of farms in the South West. Of 888 sheep flocks tested in Devon so far only eight have tested positive for foot and mouth antibodies. These tests are necessary to 'clean' an area before movement restrictions can be lifted. On one farm only one sheep who tested positive was culled. The rest of the flock escaped slaughter after testing negative. Does this suggest common sense rules rather than blanket slaughter?

The silage team arrived at 10 this morning and hope to clear 100 acres in one day. When we made our own silage we could only harvest 20 acres a day. Five tractors and trailers are hauling down from the hill due to the distance involved. Drove very slowly along our lane as a tractor fully loaded would weigh 12 tonnes and not be able to stop in a hurry.

Having collected the fertile Light Sussex eggs, Sam and I set up the two broody hens in two separate rabbit hutches last night. Rather than risk those precious eggs we sat them on old eggs overnight. This would confirm whether they were truly broody. Good news. Both hens are sitting tight. Gently poked the eggs under the hens, eight each. A quick shuffle from the hen to get them comfortable and only three weeks to wait. One of the broody hens is an ex-battery cage hen. This is unusual as 'going broody' has been bred out of commercial hens. It is good to see nature winning through.

The white hen has hatched six new chicks, much to Sam's delight. One egg showed a small hole where the chick had tried to chip its way out but failed and died. I peeled off the remainder of the shell. It is a miracle to see how the chick rolled up so tight fills every available space.

Bought four fertile duck eggs in market this morning as Sam is desperate for ducklings. Now to find another broody hen. There is a little black bantam hen but I think the eggs are bigger than her.

The silage team finish at 10 p.m. Over 600 tonnes of grass in the pit. Took out tea to the team as it always boosts morale. A good day's work. That will cost us over £4,000 just to bring in the silage.

July

Sunday 1 July. Attended family service to watch the children performing a shorter version of *Joseph*. Duncan had to stay at home to sheet the silage pit.

Church packed due to visitors from Scotland. Spoke to a farmer's daughter from the Borders who described the quiet and empty fields at home. Where once ewes would call their lambs to order there is silence. The grass continues to grow but the dilemma is whether the year's silage and hay can be used. Is it virus-free? Can it be fed to sheep and cattle when the farms are allowed to restock?

Spent all day paying farm bills. The money we received for the calves has gone straight back out again to clear debts from earlier in the year.

The last calf born, an Aberdeen Angus heifer, has gone missing. Having brought Mum in for milking, the calf went into hiding somewhere in the valley fields. On our own it could take hours to find the calf. Decided to take the cow, No 22, out with us. She'll find her own calf. True to form, the cow lead us into Bramble Close and on cue the calf, in response to her call, jumped out of the hedge. Success. As the calf had had to wait two days for her tea Sam duly christened her Patience.

With a promise of a fish and chip supper the children helped Duncan sheet down the pit after tea. The pit has to be totally sealed to keep all air out. We buy giant black plastic sheets, measuring say 100 feet by 45, and then cover the pit with old car tyres.

It is not much fun in hot weather as the sheets reflect the heat and the tyres, having been stacked all year, are full of stagnant water. Both children become smelly and soaked. However, I feel Sam slightly overreacted when he came back in saying 'I'm never going to be a farmer. It's a horrible job. It's worse than giving birth'.

Monday 2 July. The county was clear of any outbreaks yesterday. A positive step forward, thank goodness.

We have all had enough of carrying heavy buckets of water day and night to the calves. The solution is to turn them all into the inner yard shed where there is a big mains water trough. Duncan hired our neighbour's machine to clean out the shed but trying to keep back 20 inquisitive calves every time we opened the gate tested our patience. Finally we left the calves racing round the shed, glad of the freedom. A job well done.

Tuesday 3 July. Up early to attend a stand at the Hampton Court Flower Show. Having followed the advice to diversify we are agents in the South West for an excellent steel lawn edging.

With so many other shows being cancelled, traders described how turnover has crashed. One nurseryman from Yorkshire described how his whole dale has been infected. In his daily ten-mile route he now rarely sees or hears any animal. A friend on the stand described how, when the local Army officer from Catterick took up his post in Yorkshire, three weeks after the first outbreak, his office had one secretary, one telephone and not a single map. No wonder there were delays.

Returned late only to discover the cows had been without water in the searing heat until Mike used all his Heath Robinson skills to bodge the job, but with success. Alice, having fainted twice at school, was taken to hospital by ambulance. What a day to be away.

Wednesday 4 July. What an incredible night. The intensity of the thunder and lightning raged for three hours. It seemed the sky was permanently alight. First the terrified dog dived under our bed, closely followed by two frightened children. Alice cried that she had left Misty out tonight. That worried me as I had no idea how she would cope. She had gone out with the herd so perhaps there was safety in numbers.

Four in a bed and we overslept. No electricity but the pony is quietly grazing in the field opposite. Ninety cows are waiting to be milked. It is only now that Duncan wishes he had mended the generator. Why do SWEB not have a human voice? Answering machines are so frustrating. We are told to ring back tonight if the electricity has not come back on. Not much help if your udder is bursting with milk.

Sam's school has been struck by lightning, a hole blown in the roofing tiles.

Friday 6 July. It is encouraging to see the results of the blood testing campaign. Only about 300 of the 200,000 tests in sheep had proved positive. This means the virus is not endemic as many farmers feared but just lingering in some flocks.

DEFRA announced that it would pay the veterinary charges for farmers wanting to move livestock to slaughter. The inspections will now be carried out by local veterinary inspectors instead of private vets. This is a positive note for DEFRA and suggests it has listened to the rural voice.

We are very worried about No 108. She is the cow who cut her teat and became very lame. She has almost given up the will to live but we are not sure why. The OTMS (Over Thirty Month Scheme) brought in as a result of BSE is closed, due to foot and mouth. We may be able to book her in on the welfare scheme but the backlog is enormous. Whatever it would not be right to let her suffer.

Saturday 7 July. It is confirmed that over three and a half million animals have now been slaughtered. And it hasn't finished yet. Who could ever have imagined how many animals would have to be destroyed. It's so hard to visualise that many animals.

Spoke to the vet involved in a recent Devon outbreak. This case was confirmed only as a result of blood testing the sheep as a preliminary to the lifting of a 3 km protective zone. This demonstrates how difficult it is to detect foot and mouth in sheep. This farm had been under a form D restriction since the start of the outbreak in Devon and the stock regularly inspected by vets. Indeed the last inspection only took place a week before the blood tests. Such is the power of the virus to lay undetected in sheep.

We have separated the suckler cows and calves. Financially it is a better decision to milk the cows and wean the calves. As we plan to rear the calves there is no benefit in keeping them on the cows.

Who said the countryside was quiet? We have had to shut the cows in the shed and feed them silage. If they were allowed out they would simply walk straight through the electric fence and head for home. We have settled the calves by leaving No 33 and No 108, two lame cows, to look after them. They have taken on the role of grandmother but with sixteen grandchildren each. When it all gets too much for them they sit down in the corner. Meanwhile the calves take the opportunity to race round the shed, tails high in the air.

Spot, the pet pig who sleeps through it all, was totally unaware that she lay in the path of the race track, forming a living 'Beecher's Brook'. The calves jumped over her on each lap, a clear round every time.

Hopefully by the end of the week the cows will have settled down. Now where did I put my ear plugs?

Sunday 8 July. The impending harvest cannot escape the problems of foot and mouth. Dirty tractors and dirty farm clothing could cost harvesting farmers £5,000 in fines this summer as the authorities try to stop sporadic outbreaks of the disease.

Not all corn and straw is stored on the farm. Much is sold at harvest and needs to be taken away. Traditionally stock farmers buy straw for the winter from local arable farms or larger loads are transported from east to west along the motorways. Unless strict disinfectant regimes are enforced there is a risk of spread with so much traffic going between infected and clean areas.

On a personal level we retain all our straw but sell the corn privately to local Devon stock farmers. Contractors are used for combining, baling and hauling. These contractors will visit many different farms during the summer. The risk is very real.

Some of the 100-tonne commercial grain-hauling lorries have already been used to haul carcasses to rendering plants or burial sites. It is vital we are all aware of the dangers.

Monday 9 July. Just about to serve supper, already two hours late, when Mike drove into the yard. He had received the dreaded phone call—'the heifers are out on the main road'. The only good news was that they were not on the golf-course.

Duncan had apparently 'stolen' the electric fence used on the heifers' fence for the dairy cows. Somehow the heifers knew the fence was no longer electrified and they made a quick exit over the hedge. How did they know? Do they test it every day, just in case?

Told Duncan I would buy a new fencer. £80 for peace of mind is a good deal, I said. Duncan grumbled but was outvoted 2:1 by Mike and me.

Returned to find 30 calves out in the yard. When we rushed away they were being fed and we had left the gate open. Oh, the joys of keeping stock.

We all sat down to roast chicken at 11 p.m., now five hours late. Food never seems to dry out when left in the bottom oven of the Aga but we were all too starving to notice.

Peter and David arrived to go rabbit shooting with Duncan. Rabbits are everywhere. Shooting twenty or so is only the tip of the iceberg but makes us feel a lot better.

Tuesday 10 July. Alice is upset to discover that Pony Club Camp has been cancelled as the proposed site is in an infected area. The committee considered the risk too high. Ponies are also extremely unfit this season as riding and competitions have been very limited. But the children are still very disappointed.

Thursday 12 July. All farmers have received a video called *Stop the Spread*, outlining the risks of foot and mouth disease. Cynically, I could suggest that this is a little too late. The video contains biosecurity (where did this word come from?) instructions on how we must keep gates shut or even locked, disinfect every time we go out and ensure visitors also disinfect.

But, DEFRA, please consider that whilst we continue to disinfect and apply for licences to move our animals the country-side will soon be open to all.

Will this still pose a risk to farmers? The Rights of Way Officer in our local paper said 'Anyone stepping in dung in a field should remove it before leaving the field'. Believe me, if you step in a nice juicy cow-pat cleaning your shoe is not a simple affair. Unless that shoe is thoroughly disinfected (unlikely) the walker can unwittingly introduce millions of virus cells on to the next farm. Dogs have the potential of four feet to land in the same juicy cow-pat.

In one gentle afternoon stroll that same walker and his dog can walk through our cows and four other neighbouring stock farms when the footpaths are open.

Of course footpaths must be opened but surely limited where stock are involved. I wonder if information videos and future blanket opening of footpaths are more for political correctness than anything else. Only time will tell.

Friday 13 July. Tried to ignore the date today.

Confirmed that DEFRA want all footpaths outside the 10 km infected area opened this weekend. Confused as to whether the paths through stock fields (shown as purple Keep Out signs) are exempt. Will ring the County Footpaths Office. Somerset County Council are hoping to keep paths outside the 3 km protection zone closed until 28 July. DEFRA has produced a code of practice for walkers. Must get hold of a copy.

Pleased to read that the Over Thirty Month Scheme (OTMS) for cattle will be restarted beginning in Scotland on 23 July and in England the following week. OTMS was set up as a result of BSE to keep the meat of all cattle over thirty months old out of the human food chain.

I suspect the markets will be flooded as no cows have been able to enter the scheme since the foot and mouth outbreak in February. Cows are usually culled due to infertility, high levels of mastitis or serious lameness.

Saturday 14 July. Things are looking better for Somerset. Of the 39 blood tests of livestock within 3 km of the North Newton outbreak 28 have so far returned negative. Tests have also begun in Somerset around the Clayhanger cluster.

Tests at farms within 3 km of Wiveliscombe were negative last week. But officials are still awaiting test results at a Stawley farm after a 'slaughter on suspicion' case over two weeks ago.

The restocking of cattle has started on premises in Biddisham, the site of the first outbreak in Somerset. This is a good sign of a positive recovery in the county.

But when I read of the four new outbreaks yesterday, their crisis is only just beginning. It is only day one for them and it is a long uphill road ahead.

Sunday 15 July. Totally devastated to discover that Mike had died in the night, aged 74. Duncan is numb with shock and deeply upset. For over thirty years Mike had given him total support and loyalty.

We shall miss his cheery whistle announcing his arrival into the yard each morning. We shall miss his gentle ways with stock, his ability to know exactly where to find an underground pipe and his amazing Heath Robinson style calf-pens using copious amounts of baler twine. He always had a listening ear and a shoulder for support. Mike was a true gentleman, a true man of the country and it has been our pleasure to have known him.

Sam's birthday party today. Blessed by good weather, a bouncy castle, pony rides (guess who had to lead Misty round and round) and a glass of Pimms for the parents, the party was a great success. After three glasses of Pimms I felt more able to cope with this morning's news. With 28 children to entertain you just have to carry on.

Monday 16 July. Five new cases announced today. Attempts to isolate the disease appears to be failing as the latest resurgence in Thirsk underlines. Three new cases on the Welsh Borders are 200 miles from the recent hot spots. How is this virus spreading?

Payments under the Livestock Welfare Disposal Scheme are in chaos. 97 per cent of farmers are not receiving any money within the 21-day period from slaughter as stipulated by DEFRA. Rang the Ministry to investigate the possibility of entering two very lame cows should the OTMS scheme be full. 'You'll have to wait at least six weeks', I was told. To me a welfare case needs treating now. In six weeks time both cows would be dead, having suffered severely.

Next week we were due to go away for a week's holiday to Wales. Having found a relief milker, her regular boss slipped in the dairy yesterday and broke his wrist. It looks like we will have to cancel. Going on holiday as a self-employed farmer means having to add the cost of relief help to your holiday cost. Good relief milkers are rare and can command an above average wage.

Duncan is worn out by the relentless routine of working a 15-hour day. He has missed the local church garden party, Sam's sports day and Alice's speech day. We dare not accept any evening invitations as he is never finished before 9 p.m. Is it all worth it, I wonder? He desperately needs a holiday and a chance to have seven lie-ins in a row.

Wednesday 18 July. Ten new cases announced today. The largest daily total since 2 June. Three of the outbreaks are in totally new areas. As usual the Government has tried to play down the significance of these new areas.

On a more positive note it seems that there is hope for rare and pedigree pig breeds during this crisis. Pigs, a maximum of ten per holding, can avoid automatic slaughter on contiguous cull premises provided the owners can demonstrate solid biosecurity measures.

Is this option open for sheep breeds too? I hope so otherwise a great depth of sheep breeds and family lines will be lost for ever.

Sunday 22 July. Obviously the children are upset at not being able to go on holiday so drove to Cornwall yesterday for a 48-hour break. We still had milking cover for this weekend so determined to take advantage of two lie-ins. It is wonderful to see Duncan relaxed and able to spend time playing with the children.

Returned from Cornwall to find the Light Sussex eggs had hatched. Much excitement. As I was cleaning away the shells a little bundle moved in my hand. I rushed the cold, wet chick into the kitchen and laid it in the bottom oven of the Aga. Once again the warmth produced a miracle and ten minutes later the yellow chick was cheeping loudly. Still weak, I risked putting it back with Mum. To my delight she accepted this 'late entry' and pushed him under the protection of her wing.

Tuesday 24 July. It was Mike's funeral today. A difficult day for us all. The village church was full, in respect of a much loved man. A man not of extravagant words or gestures, but a true man of the countryside.

With a touch of humour the family placed some baler twine, a tool of his trade, with him in the coffin. Finally his ashes were spread at the top of the Six Acres field overlooking Heale Farm. It's a lovely spot, just where the primroses grow in profusion in spring. Just think, every day he'll be watching us just to check whether Duncan moves the fence properly. It's good to be able to laugh at these little things.

Disgusted to read that Mr Blair has secretly ordered a halt to the foot and mouth clean up on infected farms. It seems the cost of disinfecting farms in England and Wales is three times what it costs in Scotland and Europe. The Government's answer is to simply stop paying farmers for the disinfection of their farms. That's no answer.

Imagine a leaking roof. If it is considered too expensive to repair that roof the rain will still come in. And that's no answer either.

Mr Blair cannot run away from his responsibilities. Thorough cleaning of farms is the only way to move forward. Cleaning and disinfecting (or C&D as it is now called, yet more new jargon) closes the door to future infections and opens the door to restocking the farm and putting the farmer back into business.

Of course the Government must ensure it gets value for money. Government money is our money and £2 million a day is coming from our pockets. The fault is that financial accountability was ignored until recently. In the ensuing panic, no responsibility was taken for the costs involved. We need structure, planning and budgeting, not knee-jerk reactions.

I was told of contractors receiving income from supposedly being on three different farms all on the same day. Why has this been allowed to happen? Why have the Government not been in control?

Farmers feel betrayed that they may be asked to pay for the Government's incompetence. The ministry memo declares: 'We cannot rule out that C&D costs will be limited in some way, possibly by setting a ceiling on each farm, or even that it will no longer be carried out at other than cost to the farmer'. The image of the last straw and a camel's back comes to mind.

Friday 27 July. We have finally decided that No 108 should be put down. On balance it is probably cruel to keep her alive. Her shoulder injury is worse than we thought which restricts her movements. She is rapidly losing weight, even though we carry food and water to her.

Being ten years old she is entered into the Over Thirty Month Scheme, ensuring her meat will not go for human consumption. Slaughtering at home will be quick and painless, removing the stress of a lorry journey. The vet inspected her last night and issued a death certificate.

Mr Blair has been to Cumbria. Why does he remind me of a guilty schoolboy when he answers questions? It is as though he has his excuses ready rather than being prepared to take the blame.

If only he could show some humility we could forgive. If only he could show some emotion from the heart we would support him. But he appeared defensive and distant, determined to play down the recent outbreaks and the devastation in the countryside.

Simple words of empathy and sympathy or acceptance that mistakes have happened would reassure the countryside that the Government really do care.

Sunday 29 July. The Brecon Beacons situation is devastating. Rumours abound that infected sheep, for a price, were introduced to the area. These allegations must be faced rather than leaving ugly open rumours to fester.

It is thought these Welsh sheep were infected months ago and have carried the virus through the summer. Blood tests support this theory as antibodies have been found in some ewes. Apparently the virus can be carried in the throat and will multiply and spread if the sheep is put under stress. Shearing and dipping have taken place in the last few weeks, both quite stressful for a sheep.

This hot weather will kill the virus on the ground but not any virus hiding in cow dung, damp places or a carrier animal.

4,000 sheep are to be culled in the next few days and potentially the virus threatens over 10,000 sheep on the mountains. The combination of all these facts is truly frightening for the Welsh sheep flock.

Invited to a lunchtime barbecue with friends. Pudding was interrupted when a Charolais cow started calving. Duncan stripped off and calved a very handsome bull calf. After four pints he was probably 'drunk in charge of a calving aid' but all went well.

Tuesday 31 July. Seven new outbreaks taking the total to 1,914 cases.

The situation in North Yorkshire is very serious. Sheep testing has begun on the edge of the high risk area and will move in towards the epicentre around Thirsk. Vets are certain they will find positive reactors but the level of infection will determine the number of sheep to be culled. They are determined to protect the three million pig population to the south of the area.

As a result of the recent test a further 1,200 sheep on the Brecon Beacons are to be slaughtered tomorrow. Tests on a further 4,000 begin later this week. It is staggering that generations of breeding and shepherding can be destroyed in minutes.

The calves are still suffering badly from New Forest Eye (an eye infection), even after regular treatments. The calves are still housed: perhaps it would help the situation if we could turn them out. Duncan is trying homeopathic treatment for this eye condition, adding drops to the water trough every other day.

One poor calf has a particularly bad infection and I had to inject him in the eyelid. Not a very pleasant job.

August

Friday 3 August. Pregnancy diagnosed in 65 cows this morning. A scanner, similar to a human scanner, except that this one is inserted into the rectum, can accurately diagnose an embryo at only 28 days old. It is truly amazing that a little black star shape image amongst a sea of abstract black and white blur can represent life. By three months the embryo almost fills the screen.

For No 96 it was quite an experience. Graham, discovering she was not in calf, described her fertility organs like a balloon that had blown up but was now deflated, 'All scrunched up and in a mess. I'll soon sort them out', he said as he fumbled deep inside. 'Lovely, all straightened out and in the right place'. The look on 96's face suggested she did not share the same feeling. Can't quite see the technique catching on at the NHS either, but let's hope it works for No 96.

Scanning is such a valuable tool for herd fertility. It is vital to get a cow back in calf so that she produces one calf a year. The scanner makes it possible to know the result of each individual cow. The best news is if she is in calf. If she is 'empty' or not in calf we either show her to the vet for treatment or leave her running with the bull. 47 cows are in calf, the first calf due 15 February 2002. Another busy time ahead.

During the foot and mouth crisis there have been severe restrictions to the Artificial Insemination Service to reduce the risk of spreading the disease. The solution was for untrained farmers to inseminate the cows themselves using a very basic technique which was also used in the 1967 outbreak. These herds have now been scanned. Unfortunately the results have not been good and many cows which should be in calf are not. This will mean a financial loss on many of these farms.

On a more humorous note, Graham rang the newly formed DEFRA two weeks ago with some queries. When asking if some semen could be moved the lady was totally confused and asked

132

what he meant by semen? He then asked for permission to move a bull from another farm in with some cows. 'Will the bull be in close proximity to the cows?', she innocently asked. 'Very close proximity we hope', replied Graham. Permission was duly granted. The South West has just been declared free of foot and mouth. May that continue to be true for all our sakes.

Saturday 4 August. Listened to Lord Whitty being interviewed on the radio. It made me mad.

Lord Whitty took on the role of Mr Squeers, the headmaster, and gave 'six of the best' to the sheep farmers. 'Never again', he said 'could they expect the taxpayer to foot the bill and pay for compensation of a million lambs'.

He hoped the farmer might say 'Yes Sir, thank you Sir', and disappear. But farmers were not going to take the blame for this one.

Before the foot and mouth outbreak 'light lambs' produced from the hills were successfully exported to countries such as Spain and Italy. Farmers had created this market from their own hard work and initiative. Now exports are banned and there is a surplus of lightweight lambs, through no fault of the individual hill farmer.

The reality is that similar lambs are imported for school meals and the menu at the Ministry of Defence. Surely we should market these lambs for home consumption. The thought that these lambs might be slaughtered but then dumped abhors me. Somewhere our priorities are wrong.

A local farmer with an airfield refused the Ministry of Defence permission to use the airfield for 'exercises' until they changed their policy over the use of foreign meat. How satisfying to have some power to react. Good for him.

Alice is keen to try out a new pony the 'next size up'. Harvey, as he is called, lives in deepest foot and mouth country in Devon. Duncan, never that keen on ponies, is unsure whether we should drive to see him. With the constant pressure of a very determined daughter who has already disinfected the car he stands no chance and we drove into Devon to meet Harvey.

Monday 6 August. 'Don't cry Mr Farmer, you're a millionaire, all your worries are over'. It seems that Mr Blair has released his army of moles to undermine British agriculture. As chief mole, he has done his best to build a network of mistrust and doubt between the farmer and the taxpayer. It appears that the size of the compensation cheques have shocked ministers and embarrassed the NFU. The fundamental point is that these animals were slaughtered by a government ruling. Why are the NFU embarrassed? Surely they knew that all animals are valued by a valuer appointed and paid for by the Government. The valuer will consider the high pedigree value of the stock, the stage of the market cycle and the demand at the time.

If your house was in the path of a new London airport you would be offered compensation and probably an allowance for legal fees too. You too may become a cash millionaire but only until you bought your new home.

Yes, some farmers are compensation millionaires but only until the point they reinvest and restock the farm. Some may choose not to do so. Likewise you may prefer not to buy another house, but invest your money and rent. It's a matter of personal choice.

And what of the consequential loss? Friends of ours in Devon, who lost everything in April, are probably one of these 'millionaires' but for over three months they have received no income. In that time they have lost over £90,000 in milk income, £50,000 in potential lamb sales and over £12,000 in lost calves. Obviously it is not all profit, but the effect on cash flow is devastating.

They may not be able to restock until next spring. Consider, they will have lost nearly a year's income. For every 'millionaire critic', ask them if they could live without their salary for a year?

Labour is indulging in farmer-bashing to distract attention from their own inadequacies. To quote a national newspaper: 'Before the election the Government wept crocodile tears for the farmers. Now it is baring its teeth'.

Tuesday 7 August. I can't believe it. The heifers and bull have broken out again. Why? They have 15 acres of fresh, lush grass but choose instead to walk through a fence and into the woods. This tests Duncan's patience. After two hours of searching through the woods, Duncan and I return to the farm for afternoon milking. Surprise, surprise. The milking herd have visitors. The now unpopular young stock have walked home to join the herd. The problem is we now have two bulls in one field. Reminiscent of Tyson v. Bruno, the fight began. We shut the gate and left them to it, although Duncan wanted to separate them.

A simple gate wasn't going to stop these two. Breaking the gate down, they continued their fight in the yard watched by a herd of adoring fans.

Duncan suggested we split the bulls but when the big Charolais bull strode towards me and the gate, shaking his head, I was terrified. Through tears of fear and anger with Duncan for being so stupid, we finally separated them. I was annoyed with Duncan as he can see no danger in the situation and would not even carry a fork or metal bar.

Having been involved with two different families where a bull had killed a man in both cases I have enormous respect for the strength of a bull. Generally a bull in a herd, in a routine, is no problem. It is when the routine is changed in some way that you must be aware of the danger.

We read that Mrs Beckett is away caravanning in France for five weeks. How do I feel about that? I do envy the time she is away. Five weeks—Duncan would dream of five days. I do wonder if a new girl in a new job should be away from her office until September, whilst so many animals are still being destroyed. Do her actions send the right message to farming and tourist businesses?

I suspect the farmers can't imagine a five-week holiday and the hoteliers wonder why she didn't park her caravan on their site.

Wednesday 8 August. Have had to arrange a licence to move the heifers and bull back up on to the hill. The vet will have to come out and inspect the stock. What a lot of effort and red tape when you consider the countryside is open to everyone else.

The bulls have sorted their pecking order. The little black bull is definitely number two with a bruised left eye to prove it.

'The fox gets it'. Head count of chicken shows he is still taking one hen a day. Whereas we had 20 red hens, we now only have two. Enough is enough so decide to set up an electric fence in the chicken paddock. Alice and Sam both very helpful (wonder what they want?) and by 9.45 p.m. we have cleared the site and set up a six-strand electric fence.

Sadly I have had to turn down a trip to see the gardens at Highgrove House because of foot and mouth restrictions. Anyone in contact with farm livestock over the past month is asked not to attend. I would gladly stay in a hotel for a month, Duncan ... some hope.

Friday 10 August. Desperate to make some hay but the rain is spoiling the grass. If the showers continue we may have to bale the grass for bedding, not as hay for feeding.

Livestock are returning to some farms in Devon for the first time since stock were slaughtered in early March. This will be a long process of recovery for many farms.

Before total restocking is allowed a small number of animals, acting as sentinel animals (disease indicators) are put back on the farm. This is after the farm has been thoroughly cleansed and disinfected (with government approval, of course).

The new stock from outside the infected area are inspected before they come on to the farm and then weekly. After four weeks they are blood tested. Only if all the results are proved to be negative then the farm will have the foot and mouth restrictions lifted and able to restock completely.

Good to see that meat sales are on the increase. Supermarkets tell us that 'support for the farmers' has been the biggest issue when people are buying meat during the foot and mouth crisis. Good labelling ensures the consumer is buying a British product. Thank you.

Monday 13 August. Panic this afternoon when our beloved collie, Moss, ran away during a thunderstorm. After four hours of searching (not what I had planned for the afternoon) we discovered she had been found and handed in to the local police station. Much relief, especially as we did not have to pay the recovery fee of £55.

Tuesday 14 August. The combines are rolling. Harvest has begun. This is always such an exciting time. The corn is coming off the combine at 16 per cent moisture in perfect conditions. The moisture determines whether the corn has to be dried or not. A moisture of 17–18 per cent or over means corn will not safely store but will slowly heat up and deteriorate. Drying corn is time consuming and costly, so ideally we only harvest corn at the right moisture.

It seems we are to have ten inquiries but three main ones. One inquiry to cover the 'lessons to be learnt from the handling of the outbreaks', one 'scientific review' and a 'commission on the future of farming and food preparation'.

What's wrong with a straightforward public inquiry which has full access to minsters who were in charge of the foot and mouth outbreak? The feeling is so strong in rural communities that a petition for a full public inquiry is being launched by rural newspapers.

Wednesday 15 August. Today we have received some advice from Lord Haskins (you know, the millionaire buddy of Tony with his finger in the fat and juicy supermarket pie) who has been appointed 'Rural Affairs Coordinator' with a brief to shake up the farming industry.

From what he has said so far he lacks the bedside manner of a good coordinator. He suggests firstly we should be more like the successful French farmers (would he really advocate a return to political action or blockaded petrol refineries?) and secondly help ourselves more by getting a second job.

As Duncan started work yesterday at 6.30 a.m. and we finally took the cows down the road in the dark at 11 p.m., he would just have time to dash to Sainsbury's for the midnight shift, stacking shelves. Interesting idea, Lord Haskins.

Lord Haskins's appointment has been linked to putting a fox in charge of the hen house.

Friday 17 August. Drove Alice down to Cornwall today to help at the Dairyland Farm Park for a few days. Tomorrow, Dairyland is hosting the last of three 'Big Breakfast' events held over three consecutive Saturdays.

These have been marvellous events combining a superb locally produced breakfast and a fund-raising event for the foot and mouth crisis. All the food has been donated by local producers, growers and butchers.

Even though Mr Blair is in Cornwall he has refused an invitation to attend the breakfast from the Cornish Tourist Board, the Newquay Business Association and Anthony Gibson of the NFU. But Sam would not be put off, he felt he should be there and decided to ring Mr Blair at the Carlyon Bay Hotel.

Announcing that Mr Blair was out, the receptionist asked if Sam would like to leave a message. Sam read from the script he had written himself:

> My name is Sam Leaney and I am 10 years old. I would like to invite Mr Blair to the Big Breakfast at Dairyland at 8.00 a.m. tomorrow morning. I am a farmer's son and think Mr Blair should come and support the farmers. Thank you.

Well done Sam. That took some nerve. Will he get an answer I wonder?

Monday 20 August. It is six months since the first outbreak of foot and mouth was discovered at an Essex abattoir. The dreadful figures for foot and mouth read as follows:

Confirmed cases	1,960
Extra cases occurred within dangerous contact culls	1,450
Animals slaughtered	3,750,000
Animals slaughtered on welfare scheme	1,280,000
Animals awaiting slaughter	20,000
Carcasses awaiting disposal	9,000
Total number of affected premises	9,144

What we must not do is to allow these figures to become purely statistics. Each affected premise has a story to be told, each one of the animals slaughtered deserves to be remembered.

For me, the most horrific part of this whole terrible crisis has been the suffering of the animals. Never must life be wasted on such a scale again. The image of a flock of proud ewes bringing their lambs down off the hills, unwittingly to slaughter, will haunt me forever. Never again must we let day-old lambs die in the mud or drown in the floods purely because a welfare scheme couldn't cope.

Farmers are marching on Downing Street today to demand a full and public inquiry into the foot and mouth crisis. As David Handley, chairman of the Farmers for Action Group, said, 'This is not a day out—this is a day of action … '. We must not let these animals have died in vain.

Final Thoughts

Is it really only six months since the first outbreak was discovered? Foot and mouth has caused so much misery and dominated our lives for so long it seems like six years, not six months. So much has changed since February. How many times I have heard the reason given as 'Oh, it's because of foot and mouth ... '? The worry is that as summer fades into autumn the conditions will be more favourable for the virus to spread.

Although at Heale Farm we have, thank God, escaped the virus and the West Country has been declared 'free', the misery continues for hundreds of families. For the two families confirmed as positive outbreaks yesterday it is Day One of their crisis and their living hell will continue well into next year.

In June MAFF became a victim of its own 'contiguous cull' and was no more. Nick Brown and his team were reshuffled and told to hang up their wellies.

Was this to be a new beginning, as hopes were high, or was it in fact as many feared a wolf in sheep's clothing? A new ministry, the all-singing, all-dancing Department for Environment, Food and Rural Affairs (DEFRA) was created. I only hope it isn't 'Determined to Eliminate Family and Rural Activities'. It was hoped the new ministry could be a new beginning in farmer–ministry relations. I could describe the relationship as one of 'separate bedrooms'. Spin and seeds of doubt fuel mistrust.

Labour's spin has gained momentum throughout this crisis. Farmers have been subjected to a three-week barrage of unrelenting and highly critical Downing Street media spin. The Government has tried to pull public opinion around to an anti-farmer position.

To shift attention away from the Government and back on to the farmers was by no coincidence engineered weeks before the announcement of the inquiries into foot and mouth. Although very well orchestrated I think the Government have in fact scored an own goal, as the public have had the sense to think for themselves

140

and sort out fact from fiction.

So we are to have ten separate inquiries into the foot and mouth crisis. I'm confused. Is it really necessary to have ten inquiries, all behind closed doors?

With most of the evidence to be heard in private and only the findings published, no wonder the Government are being accused of a cover-up. No wonder farmers are marching on Downing Street. I would love to have been with them today.

The rural community is deeply hurt and deeply scarred. Surely a full public inquiry would be seen as an olive branch, the first positive step to rebuilding confidence and trust between all parties involved.

Saving face and saving political careers must be sacrificed. Animals have paid that price so ministers and officials must be prepared to put their heads on the block. I was always taught that saying 'Sorry' is not necessarily backing down but paving the way to moving on. I wonder if some government ministers were taught the same morals.

The inquiry will be able to request evidence from all ministers, including Mr Blair, but because it is not a statutory investigation, witnesses will not be compelled to appear. If they do attend they will not have to give evidence on oath. The chairmen of the inquiries have no powers of compulsion and cannot order the release of government documents.

I suspect that the effect of having these separate inquiries is simply that some fundamental questions will get neither asked nor answered. How easy for one inquiry to pass the buck to the other two. Siblings do it quite naturally so I guess nothing different will happen here.

Who decides which question is asked at which inquiry? Surely questions are so interwoven that they simply cannot be answered in isolation.

But fundamental questions do need to be answered and people held accountable. For example:

How did the foot and mouth outbreak start and the disease arrive at Bobby Waugh's farm in Northumberland?

Did the virus come in on imported meat supplies, either legal or illegal? Why is this still allowed to happen? What is the policy to review British import controls?

Why were MAFF not aware that an outbreak was unlikely to remain confined to one single region given the incubation time before it is detected in sheep?

Why was there a three-day delay in suspending the movement of all livestock, allowing the disease to spread so rapidly? We know during that crucial time lorry loads of sheep were purchased in Longtown, Cumbria, the biggest sheep market in Europe, and delivered to Devon and Wales.

Why was the epidemic allowed to run riot in the sheep population for three weeks before it was discovered?

If the disease does prove to have been carried in pig swill can we be assured that all swill will be thoroughly heated?

Should in fact the practice of feeding swill be abolished?

What contingency plans had ever been set up for an outbreak of this scale?

With the state veterinary service reduced to less than half the staff of twenty years ago, was it equipped to cope with a national disaster?

Why was the main recommendation from the Northumberland Report on the 1967 outbreak that infected stock should be slaughtered within 24 hours of the disease being diagnosed not implemented? In mid March, with the virus out of control, the diagnosis to slaughter time was on average five days.

What is the safest method of disposal for infected carcasses?

Did the movement of infected carcasses out of the area for disposal spread the disease?

Were the Government too slow to bring in external scientific advisors?

How did the political issue of the election blinker the Government's view of the situation? Were decisions made to protect the election rather than the countryside?

Why was there an information blackout during the election build up leaving farmers confused and angry?

Should the Army have been called in earlier? Officers claimed that logistically the crisis was more complicated than the Gulf War.

Why did the Government introduce its contiguous cull policy through which millions of uninfected animals have been destroyed? Was it in fact legal under European Union and British law to kill animals this way?

Why has there been such a breakdown in trust between farmers and officials? Why has there not been a sense of 'pulling together'?

And then the question of vaccination. Should a vaccination programme have been introduced? Would it have cut short the epidemic and saved thousands, possibly millions, of animals' lives?

Why as farmers were we consistently misinformed over the science and law on vaccination? As a farmer I admit to being confused over the whole issue.

I have two reports in front of me from two highly respected professors with some experience of foot and mouth outbreaks. One paper (from Professor Brown) states that culling animals on contiguous farms, as a firebreak, achieves nothing but unnecessary suffering. He states that vaccinated animals are perfectly safe for human consumption. Indeed meat had been consumed for forty years with no ill-effects before the vaccination ban was introduced in Europe in the early 1990s.

However, another paper suggests that all vaccinated meat must be separately labelled and cannot be exported.

The issue of 'carriers' also produces conflicting advice. One paper suggests only 80 per cent of the vaccines work and sheep can carry the virus in their throats for up to three months, with the potential to spread the disease. A second report categorically states that vaccinated cattle and sheep cannot be carriers. As a farmer who understands animals but a layman regarding animal microbiology I do not know who is right.

It is worth noting that in the past thirty years very little money has gone into research of the foot and mouth virus. Presumably, when the research cake was being divided the potential of this disease to kill 3.7 million animals at a cost of £2.2 billion was never imagined.

In conclusion, the details of how to control foot and mouth were laid down in the Northumberland Report more than thirty years ago. And how did the Government respond? By delaying. I do wonder if they were dusting the cobwebs off the top shelf to find a copy of the report whilst the virus spread out across the country.

My greatest fear is that it seems the Government has failed to take any precautions to prevent the crisis from happening again. Why is potentially infected meat still being imported into Britain from countries where foot and mouth is endemic? The UK has no effective border controls. Why can we not learn from countries such as the USA and Australia who have tackled the issue?

And what of the future? I am sure things will never be the same again as foot and mouth has scarred the countryside too deeply for the wounds to heal.

Words such as 'change', 'diversification', 'restructuring' are trendy political words but unnerve the traditional way of life. As a farm consultant, I used to visit over 90 farms. Each farm had a unique identity with different asset structures (landlord or tenant), different strengths and weaknesses and physical differences such as soil structure, weather pattern and farm aspect. The many different combinations of 'man, land and money' make it almost impossible to suggest policies to suit everyone.

The Government seem to prefer the message of the green lobby than the agriculturalists and took advantage of the foot and mouth crisis to criticise intensive farming. The truth is that high levels of infection occurred not in big dairy herds but amongst the hill sheep population, probably the most extensive system of agriculture in the country.

How many farmers will be forced to sell? How many farmers will use their compensation payments to restock? The average age of the British farmer is 57. Consider this with the fact that nearly 40 per cent of farm sales across England are to non-farmers. Does this suggest an industry that is moving forward with confidence?

And how will this affect the face of the British countryside? It sometimes comes as a shock to some visitors that the countryside we all know and love is almost entirely managed by Man. Sometimes he may use too heavy a hand, but without that management what would happen to the countryside?

For example, the exquisite harebell flower only grows on the chalk downs because the farmer has managed the landscape. Without the correct balance the flower would soon be bullied into submission by aggressive grass or shaded out by docks and brambles.

You only have to see a field of compulsory set-aside in July (before we are allowed to cut the field) to understand just how quickly the all too familiar landscape would change. Hedgerows, headlands, trees, streams, footpaths and grassland are managed, but at a cost. Will farmers be paid to manage the countryside?

At Heale Farm we are involved in our first year of the Countryside Stewardship scheme. With help, we have drawn up a ten-year plan to enhance the environment on the farm. We plan to clear ditches, dig out two old ponds, update the old cider orchards, lay hedges and set aside headlands around all the arable fields as a miniature wildlife haven. Obviously we will be paid for the work involved or compensated against the reduced arable acreage. In principle it is an excellent scheme which recognises the needs of both sides, improving the environment but not to the detriment of the farmer. So far the balance seems right.

This must be a positive step forward but will the country be prepared to pay on a national scale? Cumbria has lost over 80 per cent of its stock. What effect will that have on the countryside so familiar to tourists and hill walkers?

Do the public see us as a group of spongers on taxpayers' money? If you asked most farmers, they would rather farm without subsidies and get on with what they do best, producing high quality food. To farm without subsidies we must firstly be allowed to compete with our EU rivals in the single market, but on a level playing field. But this isn't always so.

For example, British pig farmers have agreed to give up using sow tethers this year, increasing their cost of pig housing but improving pig welfare. However, Italy and Holland will not give them up until 2008. That suggests a bumpy playing field to me.

Secondly, we are overloaded by regulations and restrictions. Every enterprise is limited to a quota which has completely removed the spirit of free enterprise. Quotas determine how much milk we produce, how many cows we keep and the acreage of corn grown. Yes, but be grateful you receive subsidies, you might say. In truth fifteen years ago, before the subsidy system, we were better off growing corn than we are today. I calculate our gross output in 1985 per acre was £360, whereas today for the same yield plus subsidy the gross output is only £290 per acre.

British farmers also receive less financial support than any others in the EU. For example, the French government claims £1.2 billion a year and Ireland £500 million a year, almost twice the £230 million claimed by the UK, although its farming industry is only a quarter the size of Britain's.

Has the policy of cheap food really worked? As a percentage of total income the amount the average family spends on food has declined every year for the last 20 years. Has this really been in the best interest of the consumer? As the saying goes, 'we are what we eat'. Have we failed to educate our children on the importance of sourcing and cooking the best food available?

Given the care, skill, attention to detail and investment that goes into producing a litre of milk, is it really right that by the time it reaches the consumer it actually costs less than a litre of spring water?

Should we as farmers make more effort in understanding the needs of our customer, be prepared to be more flexible to their needs and welcome them on to our farms?

Similarly, one good thing to come out of the foot and mouth crisis has been a greater willingness of the customer to understand farm life. My experience from writing this diary has been one of overwhelming support for the British farmer. That support has meant so much to us during the last six months.

The Government have suggested that never again will farmers be able to rely on such high levels of support should another crisis occur (God forbid). DEFRA's new ministers are insisting that farmers set up their own insurance cover.

In truth, it will not be possible to insure against a disease of which the farmer has no control of its spread or introduction. Leading underwriters state that insurance against foot and mouth is a complete non-starter since so much of any potential loss is out of the farmer's control.

In terms of the country as a whole, the foot and mouth trend is on a more positive note. Only time will tell how long the tail will last or how the autumn weather conditions will affect the spread of the virus.

The knock-on effects in the countryside are still very real, even after an area is considered 'free from infection'. The forgotten few are the farmers still on a form D restriction. All animal movements have been banned for up to six months on some farms, crippling their cash flow and balance sheet.

Animal movements are still licensed, a costly and time-consuming affair. A lorry has to be completely disinfected and sealed for each separate licence, and vets paid to inspect the stock.

Extra stock are still overcrowding most farms since markets have been shut since February. There is a possibility that markets may open later this year but under very tight restrictions. Old cows or cull cows, which would normally have been sold, have swelled the size of the dairy herd. Extra mouths to feed through the summer means grass usually shut up for winter forage has already been eaten. What will stock eat this winter? Already straw and hay prices are at a premium.

On our farm we still have over forty beef calves which normally would have been sold. Due to the uncertainty of animal trading and future outbreaks, prices are still very depressed. But still the calves keep eating and eating and eating.

As an alarming postscript to this book, the country is shocked at the new outbreaks in late August 2001 in Northumberland. In an area only recently classified as 'clear' over fifteen new cases have been declared. Foot and mouth is far from over and we must not be lulled into a false sense of security.

On a personal note, being a farmer is a dream many people search to achieve, as indeed I did over thirty years ago. In many ways it is an idyllic life: the freedom to roam, the joy of welcoming new life on to the farm, the satisfaction in harvesting a crop, the wonderful lifestyle for children—full of ponies and picnics—and the pride of running a business together. Having not been born into farming I treasure the opportunity even more.

But a black cloud has crept over farming. The trough was leaking well before foot and mouth, as commodity prices crashed due to the strong pound and the global effect of world trade. Through imaginative trading and a stubbornness to survive, most farmers have done their best to stop the flow. But for many foot and mouth has produced an irreversible hole in the trough. Indeed, for some the trough may never hold water again.

Every farmer, each an individual with his own unique farm business, will have to make a decision as to whether the trough is worth saving. True, the grass may look greener on the other side, but there is only so much farmers can face.

On a personal level, we have tried to adapt and diversify in our own way at Heale Farm. By adopting a spring calving herd we aim to reduce the cost of production per litre and cut down on the winter workload. I have dipped my toe into the world of journalism and constantly explore ways of earning money outside the farm.

We have joined the Country Stewardship Scheme and continually monitor costs.

Farmers are a proud, stoical, hard working race, incredibly protective of their own business. I will fight hard to keep my dream alive. I love the farm and the cows too much to give up without a fight, but we have to see a profit to survive.

But the Government, by their attitude, need to help raise the morale of the farming people who are facing one hurdle too many. Farmers and their children need to feel reassured that they have a future in farming.

The foot and mouth crisis has demonstrated how each section of the rural economy depends on each other. British agriculture can be likened to a broad spreading English oak tree. Each gnarled branch represents a different part of rural life. But the roots of the countryside, which lie deep within farming, both feed and anchor the rural community. If the tree is allowed to fall and British agriculture collapses it will take the rural economy with it. The landscape will look much barer because of it.

And where are we six months after the first outbreak? It is terrifying if you consider that there is no evidence that we would be any better placed to deal with another potential infection than we were six months ago. A sobering thought.

But the cycle of farming life goes on. Duncan is knocking on the window asking for help to take the cows down the road and the chickens need to be shut in. I only counted fifteen hens this morning and so hope the fox isn't having 'Chicken Tonight'. Misty is waiting patiently to go out into the orchard now it's cooler and the flies have disappeared. And tomorrow the cows will have to be milked all over again. It's a good life and I know I'm lucky to farm.

Well, I promised myself a giant bar of chocolate when I finished this book. I wonder what time the shop shuts tonight?

Postscript

Letters

Duncan and I have been quite overwhelmed by the amount of letters and calls we have received since the diary started, the majority from total strangers. The common theme is one of tremendous support for us and farmers everywhere.

It has been a very humbling experience that so many town dwellers, who are not directly affected by the crisis, have taken the time to write.

As one man wrote:

> … Living in the centre of London one dreams of the country-side, particularly of green hills and fields dotted with cows, sheep and lambs. That is Britain. The last few months have focused our minds on the fragility of the countryside and the wisdom, strength and integrity of those struggling to maintain it …

And a letter from Bristol said:

> … I just wanted you to know that others with no connection with farms, townies, are thinking of your fears for the future and wish you and your cows a safe future …

Or a very simple message:

> … We are strangers but we feel we know you. Do diary again, Sally. Keep going No 26. From 3 concerned OAPs …

We received some wonderful letters from children, in particular a primary school in Yorkshire. Children say in such simple words what we are all thinking:

> Dear Mrs Leaney,
>
> I am very sorry that the foot and mouth has reached Somer-
> set. I'm a bit worried too. I hope the disease goes away soon
> ...
>
> Age 9

> Dear Mrs Leaney,
>
> I hope you don't get the disease because you will have to kill
> your animals and that will be sad. My granddad has animals
> and he is worried too. I think you must feel very unhappy
> about the foot and mouth ...
>
> Age 9

> Dear Alice and Sam Leaney
>
> Are you scared about foot and mouth? We have a foot dip at
> school, have you? I am very scared ...
>
> Age 8

Young children have been exposed to some horrifying pictures and
news footage. Farmer's children directly involved will carry those
memories for the rest of their lives.

These views were expressed by one lady:

> I remember the 1967 foot and mouth epidemic vividly and
> how frightened I was as a child growing up on my parents'
> farm, that the disease should strike our livestock. It was
> horrifying and my thoughts during this epidemic have been
> with the farming children particularly ...

It seems frustration and anger are felt by the public as well as
farmers. Many have described how reluctant newspapers and local
radio have been to publish their views and ideas. The endless lorry

loads of dead animals have left people feeling distraught, but powerless to protest.

As one lady wrote:

> A countryside without animals is a countryside without heart. Farms and their animals are so important to us all. So many of us, whether from town or country, have felt frustration in the face of blunderous actions that we have been powerless to stop. There are many, many people supporting farmers who are filled with joy when they read of some good news amongst the hell, like Phoenix, surmounting the wicked craziness of unwarranted slaughter ...

Another lady simply described the foot and mouth virus as 'an insidious intruder ... '.

A young woman from Wales, who has been affected by local slaughtering, wrote:

> It is way beyond me how this terrible slaughter, human stress and animal suffering can ever by justified. MAFF may consider the right steps are being taken, but at such cost in misery. It all makes me so sad and I just wanted you to know that there are many, many people who do care ...

Or a strong comment from a man in London:

> You must continue writing your diary. So don't be too confident, Mr Blair ...

An elderly lady described how life has changed since she was farming before the foot and mouth outbreak:

> I used to rear calves and orphan lambs from different farms. You could borrow a tup or ring a man with a boar to come and serve your pig. Those were the days of freedom and sense. Today, each movement would need at least three forms ...

Another lady described her view of farming life:

> ... I'd no idea cows get up to such tricks. You just take a
> pint of milk for granted if you live in a town. It's suburbia
> here and the main concern is getting through the traffic each
> morning to work ...

Farmers and vets who were directly affected by foot and mouth
in 1967 have recounted many stories and passed on useful advice.

A farmer's widow from the Dales described how onions were
used to keep away the disease. Sacks full of onions were cut in
half and placed on every surface around the dairy and cow sheds.
No logical reason was explained, but they remained free of foot
and mouth in 1967 whilst their neighbours became infected.

A vet of 40 years' experience wrote:

> ... Like you, I despair over the actions of the Ministry of
> Agriculture being a step behind in the necessary action. I do
> wonder however why the MAFF rates for valuers and hole
> diggers are worth twice the daily rate of veterinary surgeons.
> I suggest they are all essential and of equal worth ...

And, on a similar theme:

> ... I get so cross when I hear government officials say things
> are 'under control' when it is obvious they are not and that
> communication is so sadly lacking ...

The support of the church and the power of prayer has given us
a lot of strength. So many letters have simply said, 'We are praying
for you'. A churchgoer from Birmingham wrote:

> ... I am a long time and contented suburban dweller, but
> spent some time as a wartime evacuee on a farm in Somerset.
> My Church, which is situated in a run-down inner-city area,
> is praying for farmers. I would probably be the only member
> of the Church to know the difference between a bullock and

a heifer, but we are all praying for you …

A wonderful, kind hearted 85-year-old nun sent me a medal of St Benedict, as blessed by the monks. The original use of this medal was approved by Pope Benedict in 1741. She herself witnessed a miracle when her father hung the medal around an animal's neck to free the cow from plague. Following advice, we have suspended the medal in the cows' drinking trough. Anything is worth a try.

Isn't it strange how history repeats itself? With all our modern design and technology have we really progressed? A booklet was sent to me describing a major outbreak of cattle plague in 1865, as experienced by the Bishop of Liverpool. As he explains:

> It is a heavy calamity. Myriads of cattle have already died. Many more will do so. The loss of national wealth and the injury of private interests are something fearful to contemplate …
>
> It is a widespread calamity. There is hardly a county in England which is not suffering. There is not a family which will not sooner or later suffer. The meat on the rich man's table and the cheese in the cottage, all will be affected by it …
>
> It is a perplexing calamity. No medicines or remedies appear to have any effect on the disease. After all the discoveries of science, after all that has been written by learned doctors, the skill of man is completely baffled. We have found a foe that entirely beats us. The curse of helplessness seems upon the land …

Have we really moved on very much? Has very much changed? The suffering and helplessness seems as real today as it was on the farms 140 years ago.

We have received so many thoughtful gifts through the post or left as a surprise on the front door step. Chocolate cakes and fruit cakes have been very welcome, especially when they formed our staple diet through long days of calving and calf feeding.

Chocolate was (and still is) my special treat. One day a bar of wholenut arrived with a note:

> ... perhaps a little chocolate for you all to share might lighten the load for a few minutes at least ...

I only read the 'to share' when it was too late. Honestly ... Concerned that I may have been eating too much chocolate, a friend Jill sent a very reassuring note with a quite yummy box of truffles. As she wrote:

> ... after Robert our son was born the midwife told me to ensure that my blood sugar levels didn't fall, as you are not so capable of 'coping' if they do. So please find the enclosed a little something to help keep those blood sugar levels up ...

At last the medical profession have approved chocolate. I am saved.

Some very kind farming friends from Kent, reading about the trials and tribulations of feeding over 80 calves very kindly sent an automatic calf feeder for us to try. Apparently, the farmer's wife 'threw her hands up in horror' at the prospect of bucket feeding so many calves and insisted we tried the calf feeder. The feeder was a great success in one particular shed. Thank you.

A printing company sent us some very smart, bold, laminated foot and mouth precaution signs to use around the farm. Such kindness from strangers.

We have been offered sunshine from Australia (to kill the virus) and oranges from Cyprus. Letters have come in from all around the world, from America, New Zealand, Australia, Sri Lanka, Africa, Greenland, France, Germany, Norway and Cyprus. Foot and mouth is truly a world wide concern.

Even though one family living abroad had their own challenges of living away from home, they still found time to write to me.

> ... I am sure your writings being placed in a national newspaper have also helped farmers' wives throughout the

country, making the public aware of the human face of farming. Hopefully, people are more able to talk openly without the shame of the problems their families are experiencing ...

The letters we received helped to remind us of the problems other people are facing. A local couple wrote:

> ... You are in our thoughts and prayers at this difficult time, as is our family in Northern Ireland rearing over 16,000 pigs. They feel very vulnerable at this present time ...

A friend who is an Army officer's wife, searching for a copy of my diary, described how:

> ... The man from the Church Army shop turned himself upside down in the wheelie bin to retrieve yesterday's *Telegraph* for me. I had thrown it out with the rubbish ...

She described that hearing news of the first outbreak in Essex on Radio 4 filled her with the same dread when, on 2 August 1990, the BBC announced that Kuwait had been invaded:

> ... I knew that, like Kuwait, foot and mouth had the potential to become a national crisis ...

I must congratulate the Post Office for delivering letters with some quite amazing addresses. Such as:

To Sally and No 26, Taunton

Sally, somewhere on the Blackdown Hills
Please find her, Mr Postman

The Diary Lady
Taunton
Somerset

To Alice and Sam
On the farm
Blackdown Hills

Full marks to the Post Office.

Peoples' love of animals, and especially cows, was very evident from reading the letters, whether they are involved in farming or not. To many farmers, the fear of foot and mouth was just too much. A farmer's wife wrote:

> I am only thankful that my husband is no longer alive to live through this worry. He so loved his cows ...

And from another farmer's wife:

> ... I was so touched by what you said as I feel for you as a family so much and all your 'beloved girls' as my husband used to call our cows. I don't think town people understand how attached we are to our cows and calves ...

Having received all our letters I suggest that, through the devastation of foot and mouth, urban dwellers have recognised that unique relationship between man and beast. Milking cows may be a commercial venture but its financial success lies partly in the bond between the farmer and his herd, and how he treats 'his girls'.

No 26, the downer cow, whom we lifted in a net every day for over four weeks, has almost reached fan club status. She has received her own letters and drawings from children. I am pleased to report that she is fully recovered, but has given up all ideas of motherhood. To stay in the herd she needs to get back in calf. As the bull is running with the cows the choice is hers.

A few readers were concerned that our heifers (first-time calvers) were put to a Charolais bull, producing potentially big calves. I would like to reassure them that we use the smaller Aberdeen Angus bull on heifers. Ease of calving is more important than calf value.

Some of the letters have highlighted the good to come out of the foot and mouth crisis. There has been a greater awareness of what farm life is really like without the frills of a TV soap. As one lady wrote:

> ... So much ignorance surrounds the food production industry in Britain and, understandably, few people are aware what life is like on an ordinary family run farm. I can't be the only one to admit to the fact that I would not survive 2 days coping with the pressures of farm life during a sunny spell when times are good, let alone 2 days in the grimmest of British winters.
>
> Keep up the good work and thank you for the fresh milk that is supplied to our doorstep every day ...

And the public are aware that by changing their buying habits they can offer constructive and positive help to farmers:

> ... As a result of the foot and mouth crisis and from reading your diaries, my husband and I have decided to buy more meat and vegetables from local sources and to shop in our local village rather than get everything from the supermarket ...

> ... Although my husband and I have never had anything to do with farming, we love the British countryside and anything to do with it. Having read your diaries, we will be more positive about buying British whenever we can and support the local farmers' market ...

> ... There is nothing we can offer you, only sympathy, but from now on we will only purchase British produce, be it meat, cheese or milk ...

In our village we are blessed with a lovely lady vicar, a truly caring spirit. These are the words she penned in our letter of support. Thank you, Christine.